INDUSTRIAL MAINTENANCE

THIRD EDITION

Workbook

atp AMERICAN TECHNICAL PUBLISHERS
ORLAND PARK, ILLINOIS 60467-5756

Denis Green

© 2010 by American Technical Publishers, Inc.

3 4 5 6 7 8 9 – 10 – 9 8 7 6 5 4

Printed in the United States of America

ISBN 978-0-8269-3642-4

This book is printed on recycled paper.

Contents

1 MAINTENANCE PRINCIPLES

Review Questions	1
Activity 1-1. Preventive Maintenance	5
Activity 1-2. Maintenance Scenarios	7
Activity 1-3. Predictive Maintenance	8
Activity 1-4. Troubleshooting Process	9
Activity 1-5. Work Orders	10

2 WORKPLACE SAFETY

Review Questions	11
Activity 2-1. Safety Practices	15
Activity 2-2. Fire Safety	16
Activity 2-3. Electrical Safety	17
Activity 2-4. Lockouts and Tagouts	18
Activity 2-5. Hazardous Materials	20

3 SERVICE AND REPAIR PRINCIPLES

Review Questions	21
Activity 3-1. Energy and Forces	27
Activity 3-2. Heat Transfer	29
Activity 3-3. Fasteners and Mechanical Properties	30
Activity 3-4. Tools	31
Activity 3-5. Ordering Motors	32
Activity 3-6. Ordering Relays	34

4 ELECTRICAL SYSTEMS

Review Questions	35
Activity 4-1. Reading Line Diagrams	41
Activity 4-2. Series Resistance in a Circuit	46
Activity 4-3. Parallel Resistance in a Circuit	48
Activity 4-4. Voltage Unbalance	50
Activity 4-5. Current Unbalance	54
Activity 4-6. Testing for Opens	58
Activity 4-7. Testing for Opens in an Industrial Circuit	60
Activity 4-8. Locating Short Circuits	64
Activity 4-9. Testing Circuit Breakers and Fuses	66
Activity 4-10. Testing Transformers	68
Activity 4-11. Testing Coils	72
Activity 4-12. Testing Three-Phase Motors	73

ELECTRONICS AND PROGRAMMABLE LOGIC CONTROLLERS

Review Questions	75
Activity 5-1. Mechanical and Electronic Contacts	79
Activity 5-2. Testing Diodes	81
Activity 5-3. Testing Thermistors	83
Activity 5-4. Testing Thermocouples	85
Activity 5-5. PLC Troubleshooting	88

REFRIGERATION SYSTEMS

Review Questions	97
Activity 6-1. Refrigerant States	103
Activity 6-2. Temperature-Pressure Charts	105
Activity 6-3. Compressors	108
Activity 6-4. Condensers	109
Activity 6-5. Evaporators	112
Activity 6-6. Hot-Gas Defrost	116
Activity 6-7. Temperature Control	117
Activity 6-8. Heat Pumps	118
Activity 6-9. Chilled Water Systems	120
Activity 6-10. Cooling Towers	121
Activity 6-11. Taking Pressure Readings	123
Activity 6-12. Evacuating Systems	125
Activity 6-13. Liquid Charging Systems	127
Activity 6-14. Vapor Charging Systems	128
Activity 6-15. Leaks	129

BOILER SYSTEMS

Review Questions	131
Short Answer Questions	137
Activity 7-1. Heating Systems	139
Activity 7-2. Low Water Fuel Cutoff	141
Activity 7-3. Steam Traps	142
Activity 7-4. Natural Gas Line	143
Activity 7-5. Flame Scanner Failure	144
Activity 7-6. Water Column and Gauge Glass Blowdown	145
Activity 7-7. Boiler Blowdown	146
Activity 7-8. Low Water in the Boiler	148
Activity 7-9. High Water in the Boiler	150
Activity 7-10. Boiler Overpressure	152

HEATING, VENTILATING, AND AIR CONDITIONING SYSTEMS

Review Questions	155
Short Answer Questions	159
Activity 8-1. Air Handler Operation	161
Activity 8-2. Variable Air Volume Box	163
Activity 8-3. Building Pressures	165
Activity 8-4. Filters	166
Activity 8-5. Valve Signals	167
Activity 8-6. Three-Way Valve	168

MECHANICAL SYSTEMS

Review Questions   169
Activity 9-1. Lubrication   175
Activity 9-2. Bearings   177
Activity 9-3. Mechanical Drive Systems   178
Activity 9-4. Belt Tensioning   179
Activity 9-5. Alignment   180

FLUID POWER SYSTEMS

Review Questions   183
Activity 10-1. Pump Operation   189
Activity 10-2. Pressure and Flow Control Valves   191
Activity 10-3. Unloading Valves   194
Activity 10-4. Directional Control Valves   196
Activity 10-5. Pneumatic Systems   198

TROUBLESHOOTING

Review Questions   199
Activity 11-1. Garage Door Opener   203
Activity 11-2. Motor Control Circuit   205
Activity 11-3. Heating Element Control   206
Activity 11-4. Paint Can Filling Operation   208
Activity 11-5. PLC Inputs and Outputs   210
Activity 11-6. Refrigeration Problems   212
Activity 11-7. HVAC Troubleshooting   216
Activity 11-8. Coal Grinder   217
Activity 11-9. Stopped Conveyor   219
Activity 11-10. Hydraulic Power Circuit   221

FINAL EXAM   223

APPENDIX   229

Introduction

Industrial Maintenance Workbook is designed to reinforce the concepts in, and provide system troubleshooting activities for, the material presented in *Industrial Maintenance*, 3rd Edition. When studying the textbook, pay particular attention to italicized terms, illustrations, and examples. The workbook is composed of questions reviewing these key elements and incorporating them into problem-solving activities.

Review Questions

The workbook contains 11 sections of Review Questions. Each section of Review Questions is a series of multiple choice, true/false, completion, and matching questions based on the text and illustrations in the corresponding chapter of the textbook. Always study the assigned chapter of the textbook thoroughly before completing the Review Questions.

Activities

The workbook contains 84 Activities developed from the 11 chapters of the textbook. Activities provide opportunities to apply the concepts and theory in the textbook to practical maintenance and troubleshooting problems. See the Table of Contents for a complete listing.

Final Exam

The Final Exam is developed from a selection of Review Questions from each of the chapters. The Final Exam is designed to test basic knowledge of maintenance management, building systems, and troubleshooting.

Appendix

The Appendix contains forms that support hands-on exercises in preventive maintenance, work order planning, and troubleshooting. This provides a valuable supplement to the written activities when students begin working in maintenance facilities and continue learning with on-the-job training. See page 229 for a complete listing of forms in the Appendix.

Related Information

Information presented in *Industrial Maintenance*, 3rd Edition, and *Industrial Maintenance Workbook* addresses common maintenance topics for several types of building systems. Additional training material related to these systems is available in other American Technical Publishers products. For information about these products, visit the American Technical Publishers web site at www.go2atp.com.

The Publisher

Name _____ Date _____

Industrial Maintenance

_____ **1.** Maintenance personnel are broadly classified as ___ or multiskilled.

_____ **2.** Maintenance-personnel jobs are defined by the specific job titles and numbers in the ___.
- A. *Occupational Work Areas*
- B. *Occupational Fields*
- C. *Occupational Titles*
- D. none of the above

_____ **3.** ___ maintenance is scheduled work required to keep equipment in peak operating condition.
- A. Plant
- B. Industrial
- C. Preventive
- D. none of the above

_____ **4.** A ___ order is a document that details specific maintenance tasks to be completed.
- A. direct
- B. written
- C. work
- D. none of the above

_____ **5.** ___ maintenance is work that is planned and scheduled for completion.

_____ **6.** ___ work is repair of a known problem before a breakdown occurs.

T   F **7.** A plant survey can use data from the preventive maintenance system to create a master equipment file.

T   F **8.** Electronic files are becoming more popular for storing maintenance information, as they are easy to store, organize, and access.

_____ **9.** ___ control is the organization and management of commonly used parts, vendors and suppliers, and purchasing records in the preventive maintenance system.
- A. Portion
- B. Inventory
- C. Warehouse
- D. none of the above

_____ **10.** A(n) ___ is a book or electronic file that documents all work performed during a shift and lists information needed to complete work by maintenance technicians on other shifts.

_____ **11.** Vibration frequency is most commonly expressed in ___.
- A. rpm
- B. cpm
- C. ips
- D. mps

_____ **12.** ___ is the use of temperature-indicating or -measuring devices to quantify temperature or temperature changes.

_____ **13.** ___ analysis is analysis that detects high-frequency vibrations to create an image or reading.

_____ **14.** ___ principles are based on the goal of gradual, continuous improvement in all aspects of plant operation.

_____ **15.** A(n) ___ is a sequence of operations that accomplishes desired results.

_____ **16.** A(n) ___ is a diagram that shows a logical sequence of troubleshooting steps for a given set of conditions.

_____ **17.** ___ skills are strategies and actions that allow an individual to communicate effectively with other persons in a variety of situations.

1

T   F   **18.** Successful maintenance personnel practice lifelong learning.

T   F   **19.** An energy ___ is a comprehensive review of a facility's energy use and a report on ways to reduce the energy use through changes to buildings, equipment, and procedures.

T   F   **20.** Periodic maintenance is work completed at specific intervals to prevent breakdowns and production inefficiency.

T   F   **21.** Project work may include rebuilding or modifying equipment.

_____   **22.** A plant ___ is a complete inventory and condition assessment of a facility's equipment and structure.

_____   **23.** ___ monitoring is unscheduled equipment monitoring as required.

_____   **24.** Visual and ___ inspection is the analysis of the appearance and sounds of operating equipment.

_____   **25.** ___ is the change in velocity.

Equipment Life Expectancy Curve

_____   **1.** Break-in period

_____   **2.** Useful life

_____   **3.** Wear-out period

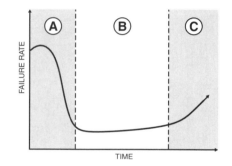

Periodic Maintenance

_____   **1.** Maintenance frequency

_____   **2.** Maintenance task

_____   **3.** Equipment description

_____   **4.** Work order number

_____   **5.** Maintenance procedure

_____   **6.** Previous maintenance work completed

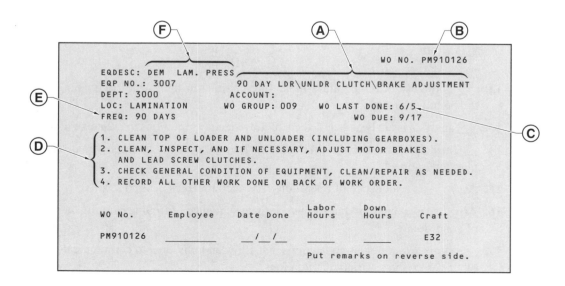

Work Order—Corrective

_____   **1.** A(n) ___ is damaged on Conveyor #2.

_____   **2.** The repair to Conveyor #2 required ___ hours.

_____   **3.** Conveyor #2 is located in the ___ Room.

_____   **4.** The ___ is to be notified when the repair is completed.
  A. superintendent   C. packing lead person
  B. supervisor   D. none of the above

_____   **5.** The priority level for this work order is ___.

_____   **6.** The damage was caused by a(n) ___.

T   F   **7.** The power was locked out to packing line #2 during the repair.

T   F   **8.** Additional 6012 rods are to be ordered.

T   F   **9.** The repair necessitated a plant shutdown.

T   F   **10.** The costs for the repair were considered to be usual.

```
                    WORK ORDER-CORRECTIVE
    Work Order:    COR 345              Description:   Repair damaged chain guard
    Asset/Equip:   Conveyor #2
    Procedure:    Repair damaged chain guard
    Requested by:   Packing Lead
    Telephone:    Ext. 556
    Asset Shutdown:    X    Plant Shutdown
    Model:    NA
    Serial No:    NA
    Location:    Packing Room
    Skill:    Level 2
    Sch Date:    Timely
    Priority:    2
    Shift:    NA
    Status:    Open
    Labor      Craft      Labor Description      Est Hrs. REF OVE DOUBL
       Maintenance      (Name printed in)
    Tasks:    ID COR 345 PR 2
       Notify Packing Lead Person about repair.
       Lock out power to packing line #2.
       Repair damaged chain guard or fabricate new guard on
          drive motor for conveyor #2 in packing area.
       Remove Lockout.
       Notify Packing Lead Person when completed.
    _____

    Comments:  2 hours.
               Damage caused by forklift.
               Rebuilt guard from mounts out.
               No unusual costs.
               Need to order more 6010 rod.
```

Flow Chart

_____   **1.** Contains set of instructions

_____   **2.** Indicates direction

_____   **3.** Contains question

_____   **4.** Indicates beginning or end of flow chart

_____   **5.** A(n) ___ shape is shown at A.

_____   **6.** A(n) ___ shape is shown at B.

_____   **7.** A(n) ___ shape is shown at C.

_____   **8.** A(n) ___ shape is shown at D.

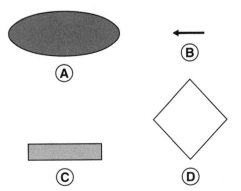

Master Equipment File

_____ **1.** Furnace #1 is located in Room ___ of Building 2.

_____ **2.** Furnace #1 has a total of ___ hr of labor YTD.

_____ **3.** The installed cost of the furnace was $___.

_____ **4.** The calculated hourly cost for labor YTD is $___.

_____ **5.** The calculated hourly cost for labor TD is $___.

T   F   **6.** There is a manufacturer's warranty for Furnace #1.

T   F   **7.** The furnace operates at 220 V.

_____ **8.** The replacement cost is ___.
    A. less than the installation cost   C. more than the installation cost
    B. the same as the installation cost   D. not given

_____ **9.** The total labor, misc, and part cost to date is $___.
    A. 5631.80   C. 14,942.00
    B. 9620.60   D. 30,194.40

T   F   **10.** The electrical service for the furnace is 1φ.

Description:	Furnace #1	Voltage:	440	Warranty ID:	IT6P882
Asset ID:	FUR0001.00	Amperage:	600	Warranty Date:	02/17
Asset Type:	Furnace Systems	Wattage:	264000		
Parent ID:		Phase:	3	YTD Labor Hr:	45.00
Priority:	8 Active:☒	Elec Line:	10	YTD Downtime:	22.00
Manufacturer:	Brown Boveri, Inc.	Air Area:	COMP 6		
Model:	IT6P			TD Labor Hr:	740.00
Serial Number:	OP2810C2B			TD Downtime:	493.00
Vendor:	Lewis Systems, Inc.	Counter UOM:			
Vendor Address:	1862 Erie St.	Current Counter:	1	YTD Labor Cost:	724.00
	Cleveland, OH 55117	Counter Rollover:	0	YTD Misc Cost:	1231.22
Vendor Phone:	216-555-1340	Meter UOM:		YTD Part Cost:	7701.19
Asset Tag:	00509	Current Meter:	1234550	Total:	9656.41
Location:	4247 Piedmont Building 2				
	Floor-1 Room 23 CL15F			TD Labor Cost:	9620.60
Department ID:		Meter Rollover:	0	TD Misc Cost:	5631.80
Cost Center:	Fixed Asset Repair	Purchase Date:	02/17	TD Part Cost:	14,942.00
Supervisor:	Jones, Fred	Install Date:	08/05	Total:	30,194.40
		Retire Date:			
		Install Cost:	97000		
		Replacement Cost:	97000		

Comment: Manufact. warranty extremely strict. Document all hours worked and parts used.

Report Totals:					
	YTD Labor Hr: 45.00	YTD Labor Cost: 724.00		TD Labor Cost: 9620.60	
	YTD Downtime: 22.00	YTD Misc Cost: 1231.22		TD Misc Cost: 5631.80	
Assets: 1	TD Labor Hr: 740.00	YTD Part Cost: 7701.19		TD Part Cost: 14,942.00	
	TD Downtime: 493.00	Total: 9656.41		Total: 30,194.40	

DPSI (DP Solutions, Inc.)

MASTER EQUIPMENT FILE

Name _____ Date _____

Activity 1-1. Preventive Maintenance

The manufacturer's maintenance literature recommends cleaning an HVAC system's cooling coils every three months.

1. If the coils are found to be clean every time they are inspected, would it be possible to lengthen the cleaning time to six or nine months?

2. What economic benefit would this have?

A production line includes both an electric heating element and a photoelectric sensor.

3. Which device would likely require more preventive maintenance?

4. Why could the heating element be run on breakdown maintenance?

One production line runs four days a week, eight hours a day. Another production line runs five days a week, 24 hours a day.

5. When establishing a new PM program, which production line is most cost effective to begin with?

5

Periodic maintenance schedules must be established for several pieces of equipment.

6. For a brand-new piece of equipment, what should be the chief source of information when establishing its maintenance schedule?

7. For an older piece of equipment that has little or no manufacturer's documentation, what sources of information could be used to establish its maintenance schedule?

8. List several advantages of a CMMS system over a paper- and file-based PM system.

9. Why must maintenance personnel complete the exact maintenance required for new equipment?

Activity 1-2. Maintenance Scenarios

Answer the following questions about maintenance activities.

1. When walking by a hydraulic system, what impromptu maintenance can be done?

2. When is the best time to search for leaks in a compressed air supply system?

3. Why is the refrigerator in the staff lunchroom run on breakdown maintenance while the refrigerator that stores chemicals used in oil analysis is inspected and cleaned on a regularly scheduled basis?

4. What should be done if filters are found to be missing during the survey inspection of an air handler?

Activity 1-3. Predictive Maintenance

Answer the following questions about predictive maintenance analysis methods.

1. What are the general characteristics of machinery that could benefit from vibration analysis?

2. Why is wear particle analysis important for older equipment?

3. Why must strict oil sampling procedures be followed?

4. What should be done if a hot spot is found during a thermography inspection of a circuit breaker box?

Vibration analysis determines that the bearings on a large, expensive motor are beginning to fail, so the work is scheduled for a time when the motor is not needed for production.

5. What type of maintenance is this?

Activity 1-4. Troubleshooting Process

Explain the general purpose of each step of the troubleshooting process.

1. Investigating.

2. Isolating.

3. Remedying.

4. Documenting.

5. At which step of the troubleshooting process are interpersonal skills most important?

Activity 1-5. Work Orders

An older motor drive is scheduled to go out of service and be replaced with new equipment when it malfunctions. The drive is critical to production, but the repair is expensive and will disrupt production.

1. Discuss the factors that would determine what should be done about the motor drive.

2. How will safety work orders be handled on this equipment?

A maintenance engineer is paged twice within 30 seconds to respond to two different production machines that have malfunctioned.

3. What factors should be considered when deciding which call to answer first?

During a PM inspection, it is discovered that a pump needs replacement.

4. What type of maintenance work order will be generated?

Name _____   Date _____

Industrial Maintenance

_____ **1.** The NEC® is updated every ___ years.

_____ **2.** ___ manages United States participation in international standards activities.

_____ **3.** Fuel, ___, and oxygen are required to start and sustain a fire.

_____ **4.** A(n) ___ is a rule made mandatory by a federal, state, or local government.
　　　　A. code　　　　　　　　　　　C. standard
　　　　B. regulation　　　　　　　　D. American National Standard

_____ **5.** The severity of electrical shock is increased with less ___.

_____ **6.** ___ is the use of locks, chains, or other physical restraints to positively prevent the operation of specific equipment.

_____ **7.** An open top space, such as a ditch, more than ___′ in depth is a confined space.

_____ **8.** Air normally contains ___% oxygen.

_____ **9.** In any emergency, the proper authorities must be notified immediately by calling ___.

_____ **10.** A(n) ___ is a substance that could cause injury to individuals or damage to the environment.

_____ **11.** A ___ hazard is the degree of susceptibility of materials to explode or release energy by themselves or by exposure to certain conditions or substances.
　　　　A. flammability　　　　　　　C. health
　　　　B. reactivity　　　　　　　　D. special

_____ **12.** An air contaminant is an undesirable element in the air such as ___.
　　　　A. dust　　　　　　　　　　　C. fumes
　　　　B. gas　　　　　　　　　　　D. all of the above

_____ **13.** A fume is a ___ from volatilized solids that condenses in cool air.
　　　　A. smoke　　　　　　　　　　C. gas
　　　　B. vapor　　　　　　　　　　D. all of the above

_____ **14.** A(n) ___ hazard is a bacterium, virus, fungus, or other microorganism that can cause acute and chronic infections by entering the body directly or through breaks in the skin.

_____ **15.** ___ is emergency care or treatment given to an injured or ill individual before medical assistance is available.

T　　F　　**16.** A standard is a collection of voluntary rules developed through consensus and related to a particular trade, industry, or environment.

T　　F　　**17.** A technical society is an organization that represents the producers of specific products.

T　　F　　**18.** Class D fires involve certain combustible metals.

T　　F　　**19.** Gas contaminants in the air are typically measured in parts per million (PPM).

_____   **20.** A(n) ___ hazard is a hazard caused by excessive levels of noise, vibration, illumination, temperature, or radiation.

_____   **21.** Personal ___ equipment is clothing and/or equipment worn by a worker to reduce the possibility of an injury.

_____   **22.** A(n) ___ is a device worn over the ears to reduce the level of noise reaching the eardrum.

_____   **23.** ___ means inflammation of the liver.

_____   **24.** The explosive range is the difference between the LEL and the ___ of combustible gases.

_____   **25.** A material ___ sheet is a document containing hazard information about a certain chemical.

Fall Protection

_____   **1.** Locking snap

_____   **2.** D-ring

_____   **3.** Lanyard

_____   **4.** Shock absorber

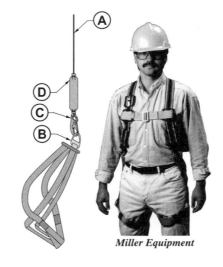

Miller Equipment

Codes and Standards

_____   **1.** Publishes the National Electrical Code®.

_____   **2.** Acts as national coordinator and clearinghouse for consensus standards.

_____   **3.** Assists with information and standards concerning proper selection, ratings, construction, testing, and performance of electrical equipment.

_____   **4.** Acts in conjunction with OSHA to develop recommended exposure limits for hazardous substances or conditions located in the workplace.

_____   **5.** Tests equipment and products to verify conformance to national standards.

_____   **6.** Tests equipment and products to verify conformance to Canadian national standards.

_____   **7.** Requires employees to provide a safe working environment.

CSA	UL	NFPA	NIOSH	NEMA	ANSI	OSHA
Ⓐ	Ⓑ	Ⓒ	Ⓓ	Ⓔ	Ⓕ	Ⓖ

Protective Helmets

_____ **1.** Class G   **A.** Special service, no voltage protection

_____ **2.** Class E   **B.** Utility service, high voltage protection

_____ **3.** Class C   **C.** General service, limited voltage protection

ANSI Pipe Colors

_____ **1.** Red   **A.** Non-hazardous gas

_____ **2.** Yellow   **B.** Non-hazardous liquid

_____ **3.** Green   **C.** Fire protection materials

_____ **4.** Blue   **D.** Hazardous gas or liquid

Effects of Electric Current

_____ **1.** Less than 8 mA   **A.** Sensation of shock but probably not painful

_____ **2.** 8 mA to 15 mA   **B.** Painful shock; removal from contact point by natural reflexes

_____ **3.** 16 mA to 20 mA   **C.** Painful shock; may be frozen or locked to point of electrical contact until circuit is de-energized

_____ **4.** Over 20 mA   **D.** Causes severe muscular contractions, paralysis of breathing, heart convulsions

Fire Extinguisher Classes

_____ **1.** Ordinary combustibles

_____ **2.** Combustible metals

_____ **3.** Flammable liquids

_____ **4.** Electrical equipment

_____ **5.** Cooking oils

Gloves

_____	**1.** Rubber	**A.** Protects against cuts
_____	**2.** Neoprene	**B.** Provides protection against chemicals and acids
_____	**3.** Latex	**C.** Provides maximum touch sensitivity
_____	**4.** Wire mesh	**D.** Provides protection against electrical hazards

NFPA Hazard Signal System

_____   **1.** Fire hazard (red)

_____   **2.** Health hazard (blue)

_____   **3.** Specific hazard

_____   **4.** Reactivity (yellow)

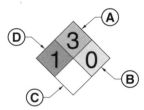

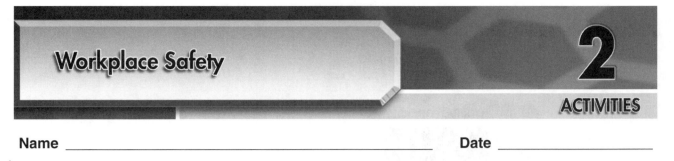

Name _____ Date _____

Activity 2-1. Safety Practices

Answer the questions based on the given situations.

1. What could be the atmospheric problem if a technician develops a headache and slight nausea after working in a boiler room for several hours?

2. What could be the atmospheric problem if a technician became suddenly weak and felt slightly disoriented while working inside a boiler?

3. Why must eye protection be worn when working with chemicals?

4. Why should an electric tool not be used while standing on a damp or wet floor?

5. What two items of personal protective equipment could make this situation safer?

Activity 2-2. Fire Safety

Answer the questions based on the given situations.

LIQUIDS • GREASE

SOLVENT CEMENT

B **FLAMMABLE LIQUIDS**

1. What might happen if a stream of water was used on this type of fire?

MOTORS • TRANSFORMERS

ELECTRICAL MOTOR

C **ELECTRICAL EQUIPMENT**

2. What types of extinguishing agents cannot be used on this type of fire?

3. How are Class K and Class B fires similar?

4. List three types of fire extinguishing equipment.

Activity 2-3. Electrical Safety

Answer the questions based on the given situations.

1. Could a technician be seriously injured or killed from working on a 120 V lighting circuit with 100 W bulbs?

2. Why is it advisable to use one hand when working on electrical equipment?

3. If a technician temporarily stops work on a de-energized circuit, what must the technician do before resuming any work on the circuit?

4. What are potential causes of arc flashes or arc blasts?

Activity 2-4. Lockouts and Tagouts

Electrical power to an area of a manufacturing plant is locked out.

1. How many technicians are working on this circuit?

2. When can the circuit be energized?

A pneumatically-actuated robotic arm in a manufacturing plant must be repaired.

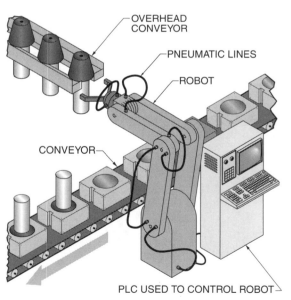

3. List two sources of energy that must be locked out for a technician to work on the arm.

The overhead conveyor is to be shut down for a major repair.

4. List two hazards that should be locked out and/or secured.

An air compressor feeding a receiver tank is to be shut down for a major repair.

5. List two lockouts that should be applied.

6. What other energy source should be released?

Activity 2-5. Hazardous Materials

Describe the health, flammability, reactivity, and specific hazards detailed on each label.

1. Health hazard

2. Flammability

3. Reactivity

4. Specific

5. Health hazard

6. Flammability

7. Reactivity

8. Specific

9. Health hazard

10. Flammability

11. Reactivity

12. Specific

Name _____   Date _____

Industrial Maintenance

_____ 1. ___ is force per unit area.

_____ 2. ___ is the rate of doing work or using energy.

_____ 3. ___ is a measure of a device's useful output energy compared to its input energy.

_____ 4. ___ is a form of energy identified by temperature difference or a change of state.

_____ 5. A(n) ___ is the quantity of heat required to raise the temperature of 1 lb of water 1°F.

_____ 6. ___ energy is energy of motion.

_____ 7. A BHP is the power available from the evaporation of ___ lb of water per hour at a feedwater temperature of 212°F.

T   F 8. Heat removed from a substance causes a decrease in molecular action.

_____ 9. A(n) ___ load is an external force applied to an elastic body that causes stress in a material.

_____ 10. ___ deformation is the ability of a stressed material to return to its original size and shape after being unloaded.
   A. Plastic   C. Temporary
   B. Elastic   D. none of the above

_____ 11. High ductile materials ___.
   A. resist stress from loads   C. fracture gradually
   B. deform easily   D. all of the above

_____ 12. ___ expansion is the change in volume of a material in relation to temperature.

T   F 13. The SMAW process uses electricity to generate the heat necessary for melting the workpieces.

T   F 14. Adhesive bonding is useful for joining dissimilar metals, plastics, and composites in manufacturing and repair operations.

T   F 15. Brazing and soldering produce joints that are stronger than welded joints.

T   F 16. Low-viscosity adhesives are liquid in form and flow readily into small spaces.

_____ 17. A(n) ___ is a rigid or semirigid pliable material placed between mating surfaces to prevent gas or liquid leakage.

_____ 18. A(n) ___ tester is a test instrument that indicates if a circuit is open or closed.

_____ 19. A(n) ___ circuit is a circuit having an incomplete path, which prevents current flow.

_____ 20. A(n) ___ instrument is an electrical measurement tool used to test the condition or operation of an equipment component or system.

_____ 21. ___ energy is stored energy a body has due to its position, chemical state, or condition.

_____ 22. ___ is the movement of an object by a force to a specific distance.

_____ 23. ___ is rotational force.

_____ 24. A(n) ___ is a substance that tends to flow or conform to the outline of its container.

_____ 25. ___ is the tendency of a physical body to persist in its state of rest or uniform motion until acted upon by an external force.

_____ 26. ___ is the measurement of the intensity of heat.

T   F   27. Heat added to a substance causes a decrease in molecular motion.

T   F   28. Fluids can be used to transmit power.

_____ 29. A(n) ___ manual is a document that contains instructions for the safe and efficient installation, operation, troubleshooting, and repair of equipment.

_____ 30. ___ is the internal effect of an external force applied to a solid material.

_____ 31. ___ is the ability of a material to be deformed by compression without developing defects.

_____ 32. ___ properties include thermal, electrical, and other properties of a material.

T   F   33. Flat washers are used under the head of a screw or bolt or under a nut to spread a load over a greater area.

_____ 34. ___ keys are shaped like a half-circle.

_____ 35. ___ is a joining process that fuses materials by heating them to melting temperature.

_____ 36. ___ is a joining process that joins parts by heating the filler metal to temperatures greater than 840°F, but less than the melting point of the base metal.

_____ 37. ___ is the measure of the resistance of a fluid to flow.

_____ 38. A(n) ___ is a product used to seal, fill voids, and waterproof parts.

_____ 39. ___ is the change in the shape of a material caused by stress.

_____ 40. A(n) ___ is a test instrument capable of measuring two or more electrical quantities.

Torque

_____ 1. A 30 lb force at A develops ___ lb-ft of torque.

_____ 2. A 45 lb force at B develops ___ lb-ft of torque.

_____ 3. A 10 lb force at C develops ___ lb-ft of torque.

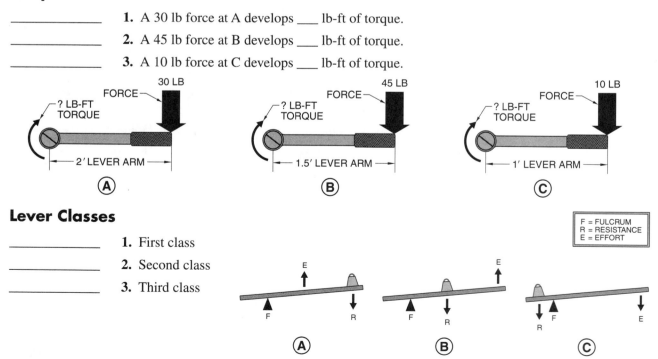

Lever Classes

_____ 1. First class

_____ 2. Second class

_____ 3. Third class

Horsepower

_____ **1.** A(n) ___ HP engine is required at A.

_____ **2.** A(n) ___ HP engine is required at B.

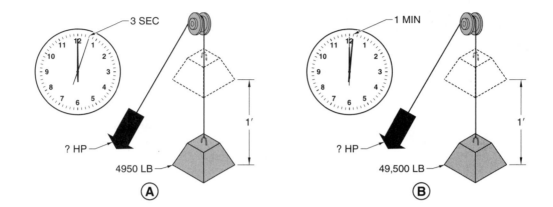

Stress

_____ **1.** Compression

_____ **2.** Bending

_____ **3.** Shear

_____ **4.** Tension

_____ **5.** Torsion

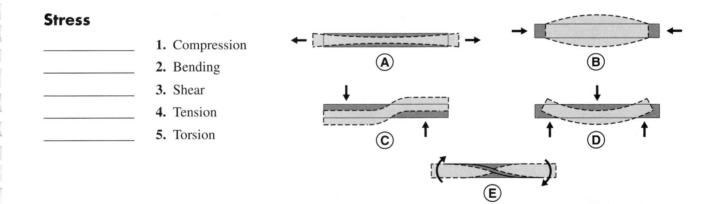

Temperature Conversion

_____ **1.** The temperature at A is equivalent to ___°C.

_____ **2.** The temperature at B is equivalent to ___°F.

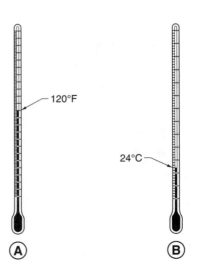

Washers

_____   1. Tooth lock, external

_____   2. Tooth lock, internal

_____   3. Tooth lock, internal-external

_____   4. Tooth lock, countersunk external

_____   5. Flat

_____   6. Spring lock

Screw Thread

_____   1. Crest

_____   2. Helix angle

_____   3. Pitch

_____   4. Thread angle

_____   5. Flank

_____   6. Root

_____   7. Major diameter

_____   8. Pitch diameter

_____   9. Minor diameter

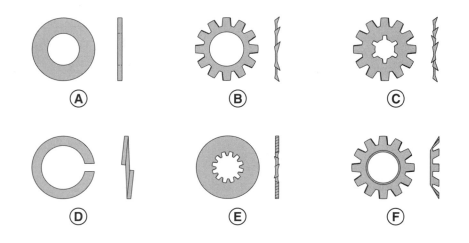

Pins

_____ **1.** Grooved, type A

_____ **2.** Grooved, type B

_____ **3.** Grooved, type C

_____ **4.** Cotter, extended prong, square cut type

_____ **5.** Cotter, lock type

_____ **6.** Straight

_____ **7.** Dowel

_____ **8.** Clevis

_____ **9.** Slotted spring, enclosed slot

_____ **10.** Slotted spring, straight slot

_____ **11.** Spirally coiled

_____ **12.** Taper

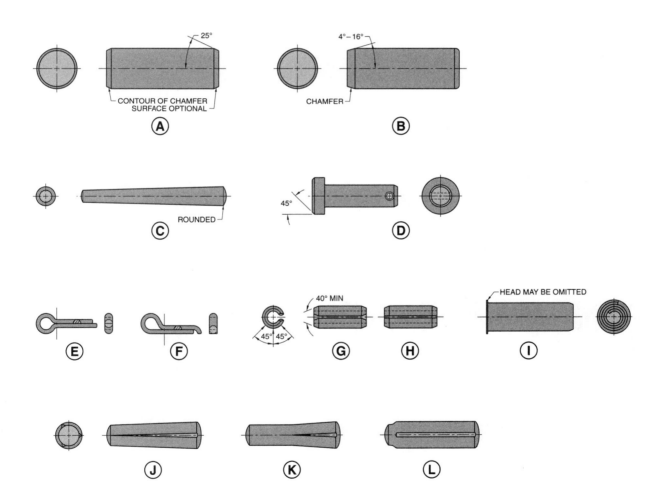

Name _____   **Date** _____

Activity 3-1. Energy and Forces

A technician is struggling to lift a weight but it is not moving.

1. Is any work being done in this situation?

2. Is energy being expended?

A safety valve is held closed by a strong spring and can be hand-actuated by a long lever.

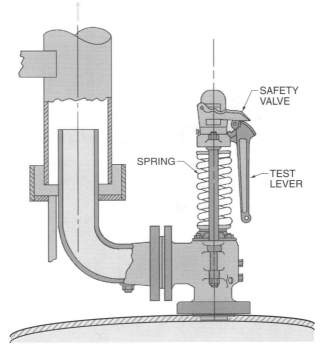

3. What type of energy does a spring represent when it is compressed?

27

4. Why must safety glasses be worn when working around compressed springs?

5. Why is the test lever designed to be long?

Two conveyors are used to transport products throughout a warehouse.

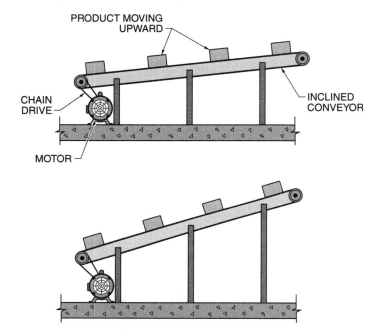

6. The conveyors are examples of which type of simple machine?

7. Which conveyor is doing more work?

Activity 3-2. Heat Transfer

Energy from the sun heats a multistory building.

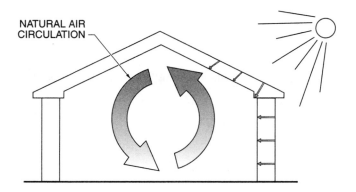

1. The sun's rays represent what type of heat energy?

2. What type of energy transfer occurs through the walls of the building?

3. Why might the ground floor feel cooler than the top floor of the building?

Activity 3-3. Fasteners and Mechanical Properties

Determine the type of mechanical stresses or forces on the following fasteners.

1. What type of stress causes a rivet to flatten when hit by a hammer?

2. What type of stress does a nail experience when it is pulled out by a hammer?

3. What type of force keeps a taper pin securely in a tightly fitted hole?

4. What type of stress will cause a cotter pin to break?

5. What type of stress is exerted when a stud or screw head is broken off?

6. What type of force is used to tighten a screw?

7. Explain the differences between welding, brazing, and soldering.

8. List five characteristics that should be considered when selecting an adhesive.

Activity 3-4. Tools

Explain the potential unwanted outcomes of the following situations.

1. Why should power tools be unplugged when they are being moved?

2. Why should operators stand to one side when starting and using a grinder?

3. Why should tools be pointed away from the body when used?

4. Why should lint-free rags be used when lubricating equipment and when working on hydraulic equipment?

5. What would happen when hammering a nail made of brittle material?

Activity 3-5. Ordering Motors

Refer to the catalog information to answer the following questions.

						NEMA			
HP	Nameplate RPM	NEMA Frame	Volts 60 Hz	Full-Load Current*	Service Factor	Nominal Efficiency	Frame**	Model Number	Shpg. Wt.
INDUSTRIAL MOTORS									
1	1725	143T	208-230/460	3.2-3.0/1.5	1.15	84.0	RS	100171	40.0
	1745	143T	230/460	2.8/1.4	1.15	8605	CI	100172	64.0
	1745	143T	575	1.1	1.15	8605	CI	100173	64.0
	1150	145T	230/460	3.4/1.7	1.15	85.5	CI	100111	66.0
	1150	145T	575	1.4	1.15	85.5	CI	100112	66.0
1½	3455	143T	230/460	4.0/2.0	1.15	85.5	CI	150341	64.0
	3455	143T	575	1.6	1.15	85.5	CI	150342	64.0
	1730	145T	230/460	4.2/2.1	1.15	86.5	CI	150171	66.0
	1730	145T	575	1.7	1.15	86.5	CI	150172	66.0
	1170	182T	230/460†	4.9/2.5	1.15	86.5	CI	150111	90.0
	1170	182T	575	1.8	1.15	86.5	CI	150112	90.0
2	3480	145T	230/460	5.2/2.8	1.15	86.5	CI	200341	66.0
	1730	145T	230/460	2.1	1.15	86.5	CI	200171	66.0
	1730	145T	575	2.2	1.15	86.5	CI	200172	66.0
	1730	145T	575	6.3	1.15	86.5	CI	200173	66.0
	1165	184T	230/460†	3.2	1.15	87.5	CI	200111	101.0
	1165	184T	575	2.5	1.15	87.5	CI	200112	101.0
3	3520	182T	230/460†	7.2/3.6	1.15	87.5	CI	300351	90.0
	1765	182T	230/460†	7.6/3.8	1.15	88.5	CI	300171	95.0
	1765	182T	575	3.0	1.15	88.5	CI	300172	95.0
	1175	213T	230/460†	8.3/4.2	1.15	88.5	CI	300111	139.0
	1175	213T	575	3.3	1.15	88.5	CI	300112	139.0
5	3480	184T	230/460†	11.4/5.7	1.15	89.5	CI	500341	106.0
	3480	184T	575	4.6	1.15	89.5	CI	500342	106.0
	1750	184T	230/460†	12.3/6.2	1.15	89.5	CI	500171	114.0
	1750	184T	575	4.9	1.15	89.5	CI	500172	114.0
	1155	215T	230/460†	13.3/6.7	1.15	89.5	CI	500111	165.0
	1155	215T	575	5.3	1.15	89.5	CI	500112	165.0
7½	3510	213T	230/460†	17.4/8.7	1.15	91.0	CI	750351	156.0
	3510	213T	575	7.0	1.15	91.0	CI	750352	156.0
	1755	213T	230/460†	18.0/9.0	1.15	91.7	CI	750171	167.0
	1755	213T	575	7.2	1.15	91.7	CI	750172	167.0
	1170	254T	230/460†	19.0/9.5	1.15	91.7	CI	750111	257.0

* in A
† Usable on 200V at 1.0 Service Factor.
** RS= Rolled Steel; CI= Cast-Iron.

1. What is the model number for a 5 HP, 1750 rpm, 184T frame, 230/460 V, 1.15 service factor motor?

2. How much more full-load current will model number 750172 draw compared to 300112?

3. Will the frame for model number 750172 work on a frame mount designed for model number 300112?

4. Why is shipping weight a concern when ordering an industrial motor?

5. What happens to current when motor 150341 is connected to 460 V compared to being connected to 230 V?

6. What should be done with a motor that is being replaced?

7. Why is careful inventory control an essential part of industrial troubleshooting?

8. Why might motors and chain links be stored near conveyors in a large distribution warehouse?

9. How can a computerized maintenance system (CMMS) help with inventory control?

Activity 3-6. Ordering Relays

Refer to the catalog information to answer the following questions.

GENERAL PURPOSE RELAYS									
No. of Mounting Pins	Use With Socket	Form	Contact Load Ratings			Coil Ratings 60Hz	Coil Current Rating	Model Number	Shpg. Wt.
			Operating Current @ 120VAC	HP 120V	240V	Volts			
8	5×852	DPDT DPDT DPDT	5.0 5.0 5.0	1/10	1/6	24 VAC 120 VAC 24 VDC	84 mA 17.5 mA 51 mA	R08AY-24 R08AY-120 R08DY-24	0.2 0.2 0.2
8	5×852	DPDT DPDT DPDT	10.0 10.0 10.0	1/3	1/2	24 VAC 120 VAC 240 VAC	84 mA 17.5 mA 8.75 mA	R08AG-24 R08AG-120 R08AG-240	0.2 0.2 0.2
8	5×852	DPDT DPDT	10.0 10.0	1/3	1/2	12 VDC 24 VDC	100 mA 51 mA	R08DG-48 R08DG-110	0.2 0.2
8	5×852	DPDT DPDT	10.0 10.0	1/3	1/2	48 VDC 110 VDC	26.6 mA 11.5 mA	R08DG-48 R08AG-110	0.2 0.2
11	6×156	3PDT 3PDT 3PDT 3PDT 3PDT	10.0 10.0 10.0 10.0 10.0	1/3	1/2	24 VAC 120 VAC 240 VAC 12 VDC 24 VDC	84 mA 17.5 mA 8.75 mA 100 mA 51 mA	R11AG-24 R11AG-120 R11AG-240 R11DG-12 R11AG-24	0.3 0.2 0.2 0.2 0.2

1. Will all of the relays fit in an 8-pin socket?

2. What specifications would be needed to order a replacement relay if the part number was not visible on the relay case?

3. What one number would supply all the needed specifications?

4. What would happen if a 24 VDC coil was used in a 24 VAC application?

Name _____ Date _____

Industrial Maintenance

_____ **1.** A(n) ___ is a subatomic particle that has a positive electrical charge of one unit.
     A. proton   C. electron
     B. neutron   D. all of the above

_____ **2.** ___ current is current that reverses its direction of flow at regular intervals.

_____ **3.** Current is measured in ___.
     A. volts   C. ohms
     B. amperes   D. none of the above

_____ **4.** ___ is the amount of electrical pressure that causes electrons to move in a circuit.

_____ **5.** A(n) ___ electron is an electron in the outermost shell of an atom.

T   F   **6.** Three-phase circuits do not always require a neutral wire.

T   F   **7.** The larger the AWG number, the larger the diameter of the wire.

T   F   **8.** All points in a DC circuit have polarity.

T   F   **9.** In a step-up transformer, the secondary coil has more turns of wire than the primary coil.

_____ **10.** A(n) ___ is a device that automatically opens a circuit to prevent damage from a high-current condition.

_____ **11.** A(n) ___ is the conducting part of a switch that operates with another conducting part to complete (close) or break (open) a circuit.

_____ **12.** A ___ is an OCPD with a fusible link that melts and opens the circuit when an overload condition or short circuit occurs.
     A. CB   C. switch
     B. fuse   D. none of the above

_____ **13.** Contacts fail when they ___.
     A. do not close   C. offer resistance to current flow
     B. do not open   D. all of the above

_____ **14.** A(n) ___ is an electrical switch that is actuated by a separate circuit.

T   F   **15.** All lamp ballasts produce some noise.

T   F   **16.** Overheating is the most common cause of motor failure.

_____ **17.** A(n) ___ circuit is a circuit having an incomplete path, which prevents current flow.

_____ **18.** ___ is the opposition to the flow of electrons.

_____ **19.** A(n) ___ switch is a switch that is operated by a person.

_____ **20.** A(n) ___ drawing contains building information in the form of floor plans, elevation views, section drawings, and detail drawings.

_____ **21.** A(n) ___ is a material that has little resistance and permits electrons to move through it easily.

_____ **22.** A(n) ___ is the smallest building block of matter that cannot be divided into a smaller unit without changing its basic character.

_____ **23.** A(n) ___ is a subatomic particle that has a negative electrical charge of one unit.
     A. proton   C. electron
     B. neutron   D. all of the above

_____ **24.** ___ is the flow of electrons through a conductor.

_____ **25.** ___ is the positive or negative state of an object.

_____ **26.** A ___ is a piece of equipment in which incoming electrical power is broken down into smaller units for distribution throughout a building.
     A. disconnect   C. lighting panel
     B. switchboard   D. none of the above

T   F   **27.** In three-phase AC voltage, the coils are out-of-phase with each other.

_____ **28.** ___ is the discharge of an electric current across a gap.
     A. Stabbing   C. Arcing
     B. Pitting   D. Tracing

_____ **29.** Group relamping is the replacement of all lamps in a given area when they reach ___ % of their rated life.
     A. 50–70   C. 80–90
     B. 60–80   D. 90–99

_____ **30.** The phases in a three-phase system are commonly labeled ___ and are energized in sequence.
     A. 1, 2, and 3   C. X, Y, and Z
     B. A, B, and C   D. none of the above

_____ **31.** A(n) ___ is a material that has a high resistance.

_____ **32.** ___ is the presence of a completed path for current flow.

_____ **33.** A(n) ___ circuit is an undesirable, low-resistance path for current to leave the normal current-carrying path through a load.

_____ **34.** A(n) ___ circuit is a circuit that has two or more components connected such that there is only one path for current flow.

_____ **35.** A(n) ___ switch is a switch that is operated by the movement of an object.
     A. manual   C. automatic
     B. mechanical   D. none of the above

T   F   **36.** Most industrial electrical circuits are parallel circuits.

T   F   **37.** Larger emergency generators are usually powered by diesel engines.

_____ **38.** A(n) ___ circuit is a circuit having a complete path for current flow.

_____ **39.** Power ___ is the process of delivering electrical power to where it is needed.

_____ **40.** A(n) ___ circuit is a conducting connection between electrical equipment and the earth.

Ohm's Law

_____ **1.** The current at A is ___ A.

_____ **2.** The current at B is ___ A.

_____ **3.** The voltage at C is ___ V.

_____ **4.** The voltage at D is ___ V.

_____ **5.** The resistance at E is ___ Ω.

_____ **6.** The resistance at F is ___ Ω.

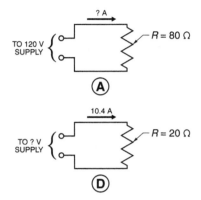

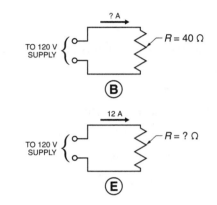

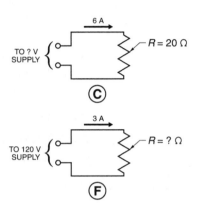

Copper Atom

_____ **1.** Electrons

_____ **2.** Shells

_____ **3.** Valence electron

_____ **4.** Nucleus

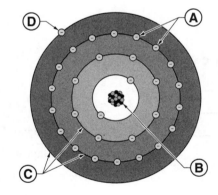

Three-Phase Motors

_____ **1.** Rotor

_____ **2.** Bearing

_____ **3.** Coils

_____ **4.** Shaft

_____ **5.** Fan

_____ **6.** Endbell

_____ **7.** Stator

_____ **8.** Motor mount

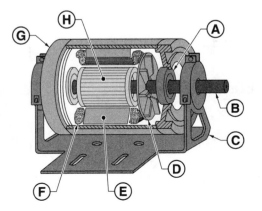

Electrical Prefixes

_____   1. A carbon film resistor with a resistance rating of 10,000,000 Ω equals ___ MΩ.

_____   2. A current of 3 A is equivalent to ___ mA.

_____   3. A voltage of 480 V equals ___ kV.

_____   4. A circuit draws 1160 mA. This equals ___ A.
        A. 0.1160   C. 11.60
        B. 1.160   D. 116.0

_____   5. A resistance of 4 MΩ equals ___ kΩ.
        A. 4   C. 400
        B. 40   D. 4000

_____   6. A shop has 100 fluorescent light bulbs at 40 W each for general illumination. The total power equals ___ kW.

_____   7. A voltage reading of 1000 V equals ___ kV.

_____   8. A current of 0.0152 mA equals ___ μA.

_____   9. A DMM has a current reading of 50 μA. This equals ___ mA.

_____   10. A reading of 1.2 kW is the same as ___ W.

_____   11. A resistance of 500 kΩ equals ___ MΩ.

Power Formula

_____   1. The power at A is ___ W.

_____   2. The power at B is ___ W.

_____   3. The voltage at C is ___ V.

_____   4. The voltage at D is ___ V.

_____   5. The current at E is ___ A.

_____   6. The current at F is ___ A.

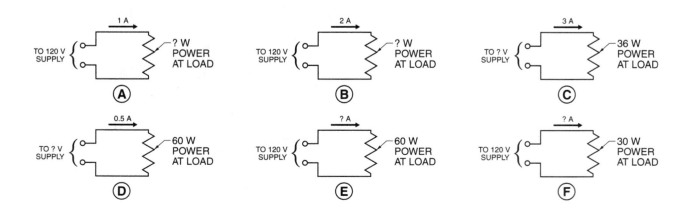

Magnetic Motor Starters

_____ **1.** Motor circuit contacts

_____ **2.** Armature

_____ **3.** Coil terminals

_____ **4.** Overload contact

_____ **5.** Heater unit

_____ **6.** Coil

_____ **7.** Auxiliary contacts

_____ **8.** Overload reset

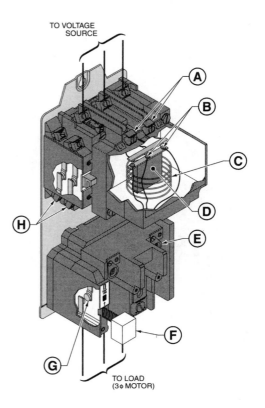

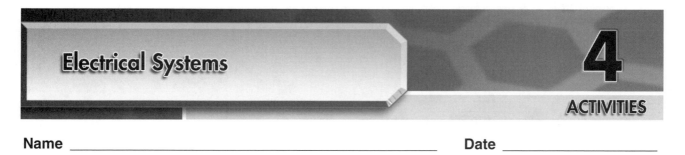
Name _____ **Date** _____

Activity 4-1. Reading Line Diagrams

A line diagram shows the operation of a control circuit. The circuit includes start and stop pushbuttons, motor coils, contacts, and overload protection. The M1, M2, and M3 coils operate magnetic motor starters. When a coil is energized, it causes the contacts to close, energizing a motor. The motor is not included in this diagram, only the controls that operate the magnetic motor starters.

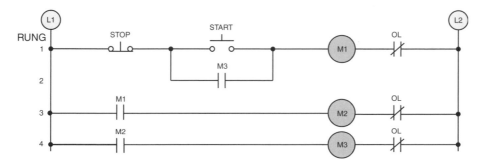

1. When the start button is pressed, which coil energizes first?

2. This causes the M1 contacts on which rung to close?

3. This causes which other coil to energize?

4. Does pressing the start button energize all three coils?

5. Will the coils remain energized when the start button is opened?

6. If the stop button is pressed, which coil(s) de-energize?

7. If the M2 overload contacts open, will the M1 coil de-energize?

A line diagram shows the operation of a control circuit. The circuit includes start and stop pushbuttons, a timer, motor coils, contacts, and overload protection.

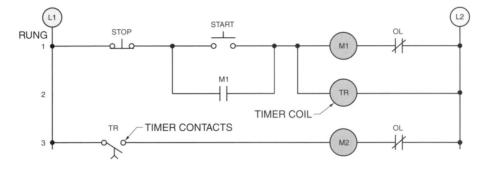

8. When the start button is pressed, which coil energizes first?

9. This causes the M1 contacts on which rung to close?

The closing of M1 contacts provides a holding circuit so that the M1 coil will remain energized when the start button is released. The motor being controlled by M1 energizes.

10. Which other coil energizes at the same time?

11. After the timer times out, which contacts close?

12. These contacts energize which coil?

13. If the stop button is pressed or the M1 overloads open, which coil(s) de-energize(s)?

14. If the M2 overload contacts open, will the M1 coil de-energize?

The M1 and M2 coils are inside motor starters. When the coils energize, the motors start.

15. If power is lost to this circuit, will the motors restart without pressing the start button again?

A line diagram shows the operation of a control circuit. The circuit includes a float switch, motor coil, and overload protection.

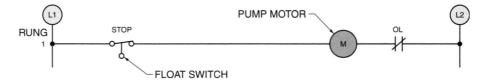

16. When the float switch is closed, which component is energized?

17. If the M1 overloads are open, will the motor restart if the float switch is closed?

18. If power is lost to this circuit, will the motor restart when power is restored, the float switch is closed, and the M1 overloads are closed?

19. What type of safety precautions should be taken when working on this type of automatic circuit?

A line diagram shows the operation of a control circuit. The circuit includes a float switch, timer, timer contacts, motor coil, and overload protection.

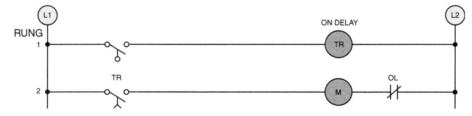

20. When the float switch closes, which coil energizes?

21. When the timer times out, which coil energizes?

22. When the float switch opens, which coil(s) de-energize(s)?

23. If the M overloads are open, will the motor restart if the float switch is closed?

24. If the M overloads are open, will the timer start if the float switch is closed?

25. If power is lost to this circuit, will the motor restart when power is restored, the float switch is closed, and the M overloads are closed?

Activity 4-2. Series Resistance in a Circuit

A line diagram shows several loads and switches connected to a power circuit.

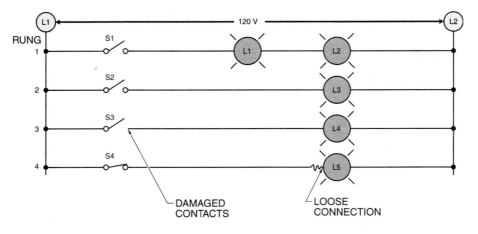

1. If both light bulbs in Rung 1 are the same wattage, what is the voltage drop across each light?

2. How would the brightnesses of the light bulbs in Rung 1 compare to each other?

3. How would their voltage drops and brightnesses compare if L1 was a higher wattage than L2?

4. If the switch contacts are clean, what is the voltage drop across S2 when it is closed?

5. What is the approximate voltage drop across L3 in Rung 2?

6. How do the problems in Rungs 3 and 4 affect the voltage available to L4 and L5?

7. What would happen to the brightness of light bulbs L4 and L5?

8. What voltage drop reading indicates damaged contacts?

9. What resistance readings would indicate dirty contacts?

10. What maintenance activities will help prevent loose connections or dirty contacts?

Activity 4-3. Parallel Resistance in a Circuit

A line diagram shows several loads and switches connected to a power circuit.

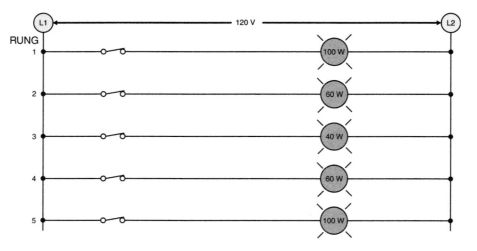

1. What happens to total circuit resistance if individual rungs are disconnected one at a time, starting with Rung 5?

2. What happens to total circuit resistance when loads are added to a parallel circuit?

3. What happens to total circuit current when loads are added to a parallel circuit?

4. What happened to circuit current flow in order to blow a fuse or trip a circuit breaker?

5. If the circuit was supplied with 100 V instead of 120 V, what would happen to total circuit current?

6. Which rung(s) have the least current flow?

7. Which rung(s) have the highest current flow?

8. What difference must there be between Rungs 2 and 4 if current flow was lower in Rung 2 than in Rung 4?

9. What would happen to a load rated for 25 V if it was supplied with 120 V?

10. What would happen to a load rated for 208 V if it was supplied with 120 V?

11. What must be done when a fuse blows or a circuit breaker opens for no apparent reason?

Activity 4-4. Voltage Unbalance

Calculate the voltage unbalance in the following three-phase circuits.

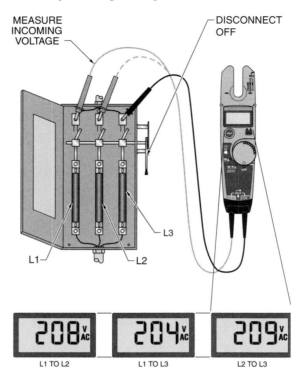

1. What is the average voltage?

2. What is the maximum deviation from the average?

3. What is the percentage of unbalance (the percentage of maximum deviation from the average)?

4. Is this circuit acceptably balanced?

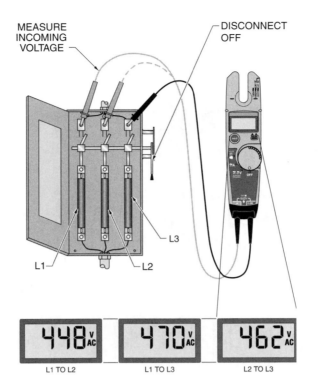

MEASURE INCOMING VOLTAGE

DISCONNECT OFF

L3

L1

L2

448 V AC	470 V AC	462 V AC
L1 TO L2	L1 TO L3	L2 TO L3

5. What is the average voltage?

6. What is the maximum deviation from the average?

7. What is the percentage of unbalance (the percentage of maximum deviation from the average)?

8. Is this circuit acceptably balanced?

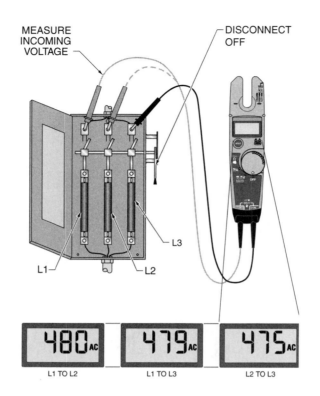

MEASURE
INCOMING
VOLTAGE

DISCONNECT
OFF

L3

L1

L2

480 AC	479 AC	475 AC
L1 TO L2	L1 TO L3	L2 TO L3

9. What is the average voltage?

10. What is the maximum deviation from the average?

11. What is the percentage of unbalance (the percentage of maximum deviation from the average)?

12. Is this circuit acceptably balanced?

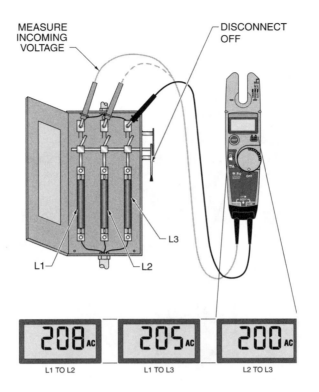

MEASURE
INCOMING
VOLTAGE

DISCONNECT
OFF

L3

L1

L2

208 AC
L1 TO L2

205 AC
L1 TO L3

200 AC
L2 TO L3

13. What is the average voltage?

14. What is the maximum deviation from the average?

15. What is the percentage of unbalance (the percentage of maximum deviation from the average)?

16. Is this circuit acceptably balanced?

Activity 4-5. Current Unbalance

Calculate the current unbalance in the following three-phase circuits.

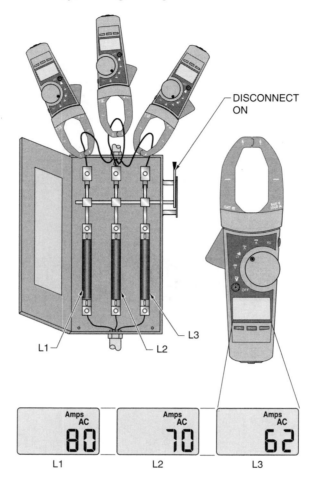

1. What is the average current?

2. What is the maximum deviation from the average?

3. What is the percentage of unbalance (the percentage of maximum deviation from the average)?

4. Is this circuit acceptably balanced?

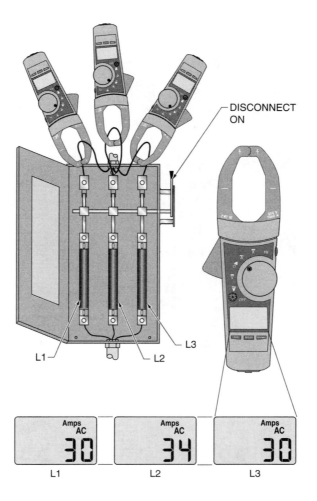

DISCONNECT
ON

L1

L2

L3

Amps
AC
30
L1

Amps
AC
34
L2

Amps
AC
30
L3

5. What is the average current?

6. What is the maximum deviation from the average?

7. What is the percentage of unbalance (the percentage of maximum deviation from the average)?

8. Is this circuit acceptably balanced?

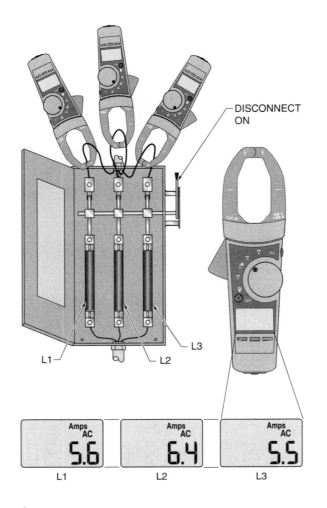

DISCONNECT
ON

L1   L2   L3

Amps AC	Amps AC	Amps AC
5.6	6.4	5.5
L1	L2	L3

9. What is the average current?

10. What is the maximum deviation from the average?

11. What is the percentage of unbalance (the percentage of maximum deviation from the average)?

12. Is this circuit acceptably balanced?

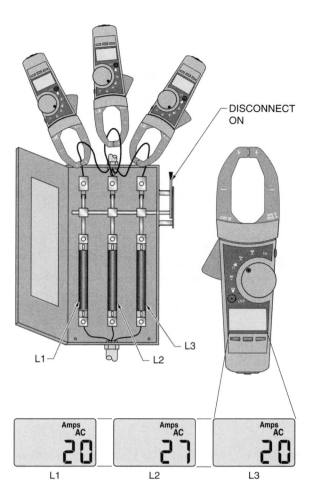

13. What is the average current?

14. What is the maximum deviation from the average?

15. What is the percentage of unbalance (the percentage of maximum deviation from the average)?

16. Is this circuit acceptably balanced?

Activity 4-6. Testing for Opens

A line diagram shows several loads and switches connected to a power circuit. Opens in circuits and loads are a common problem in electrical and electronic systems. Locating single and multiple opens in a circuit can be simplified by using sensitive, high-quality meters.

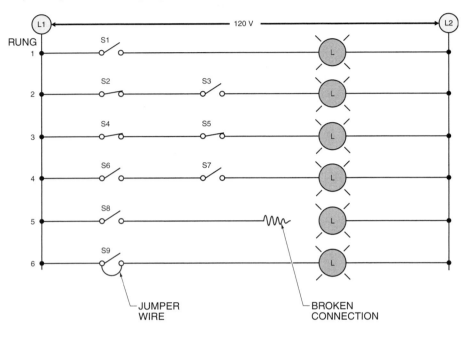

1. What is the voltage drop across S1 when it is closed and the voltage potential when it is open?

2. What is the voltage drop across S2 when it is closed and S3 is open?

3. What is the voltage drop across S4 when it is closed and S5 is closed?

4. What is the approximate voltage potential across S6 when both S6 and S7 are open?

5. What is the approximate voltage potential across S7 when both S6 and S7 are open?

6. What is the voltage potential across S8 when it is open and there is a broken connection to the load?

7. What would happen if a jumper wire was placed across S9?

8. What dangerous situation can this cause?

9. If S9 was not closing when the switch was operated, what would applying the jumper wire across S9 confirm?

10. How can a high-quality meter be used to detect multiple opens in series when troubleshooting circuits?

Activity 4-7. Testing for Opens in an Industrial Circuit

A holding tank is filled by a pump, which is controlled by float switches that turn the pump ON and OFF. The switches are mounted in the tank at various levels. A low-level switch turns the pump ON if the liquid level falls below it. A high-level switch turns the pump OFF if the liquid level rises above it. An overfill switch sounds an alarm if the pump does not stop and the liquid level reaches the overfill level. Sensitive voltmeters (or multimeters set to measure voltage) are used to test the control circuit and the switches for opens. The circuit operates on 120 V.

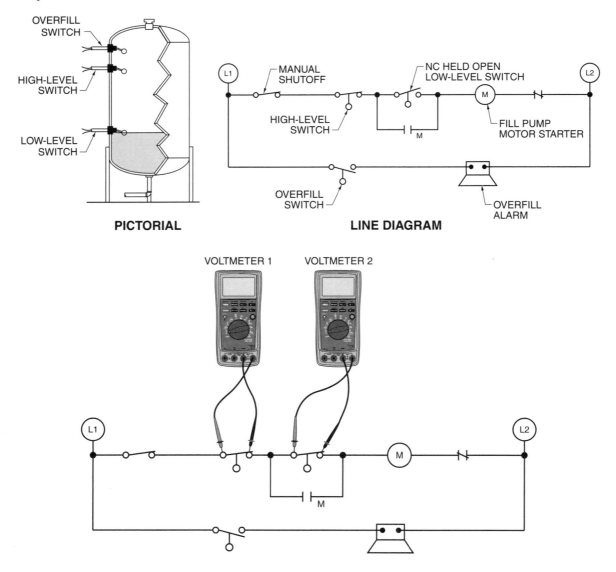

1. What voltage will Voltmeter 1 read?

2. What voltage will Voltmeter 2 read?

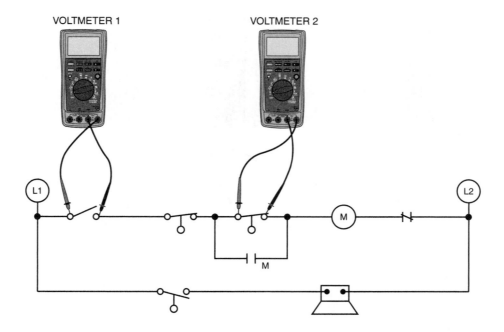

3. What voltage will Voltmeter 1 read?

4. What voltage will Voltmeter 2 read?

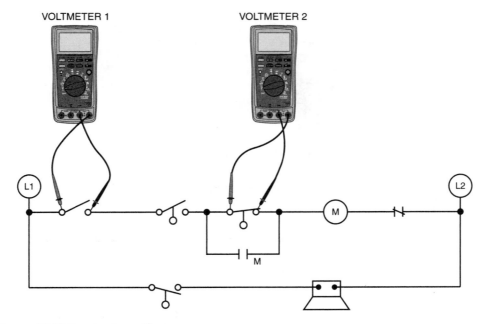

5. What voltage will Voltmeter 1 read?

6. What voltage will Voltmeter 2 read?

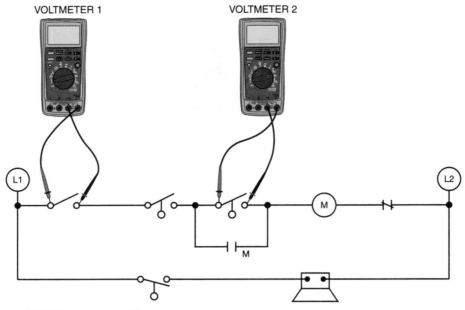

7. What voltage will Voltmeter 1 read?

8. What voltage will Voltmeter 2 read?

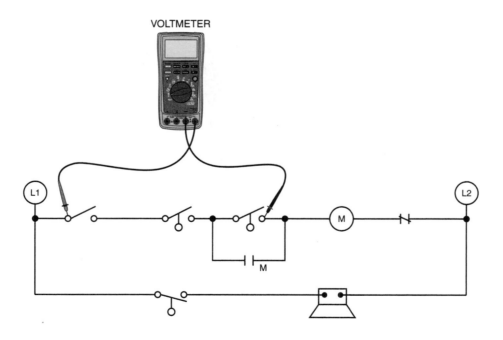

9. What voltage will the voltmeter read?

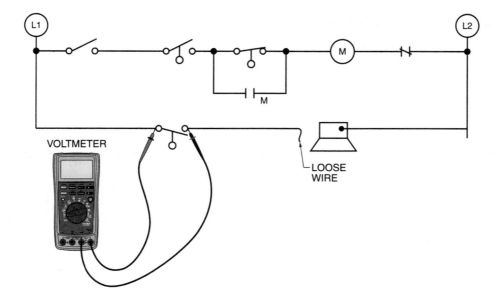

10. What voltage will the voltmeter read?

Activity 4-8. Locating Short Circuits

Answer the following questions about short circuits.

1. Why should a fuse blow or a circuit breaker trip open in a circuit with a short in it?

2. What is wrong with a circuit breaker that does not trip open when a circuit develops a short circuit?

3. What could result if the circuit breaker does not trip in this situation?

4. What maintenance activity will help to ensure that breakers will trip when there is a short circuit or a circuit overload?

5. What is a visual indication of the location of a short circuit?

6. What safety precautions must be observed before measuring total resistance of a circuit?

7. What position should switches be in to measure total circuit resistance?

8. How could jumper wires be used to close contacts?

9. Briefly describe the process of finding the branch circuit that contains a short circuit.

A line diagram shows several loads and switches connected to a power circuit. The total resistance of the circuit is being monitored with a meter. Portions of the circuit are disconnected one at a time to locate a short.

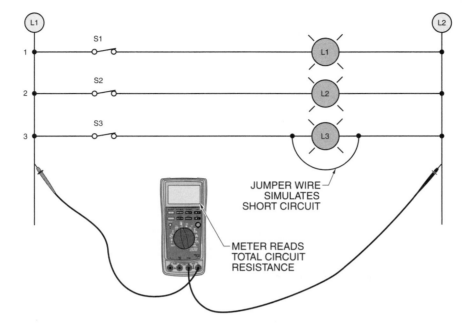

JUMPER WIRE
SIMULATES
SHORT CIRCUIT

METER READS
TOTAL CIRCUIT
RESISTANCE

10. What happens to the total resistance if Rung 1 is disconnected from the circuit?

11. What happens to the total resistance if Rung 2 is disconnected from the circuit?

12. What happens to the total resistance if Rung 3 is disconnected from the circuit?

13. What should be done once the short is located?

14. Suggest two conditions that might cause a short circuit.

Activity 4-9. Testing Circuit Breakers and Fuses

Answer the following questions about testing circuit breakers and fuses.

1. What visual indication is there that a circuit breaker has tripped?

2. How is a breaker reset?

3. How is a circuit breaker tested using an ohmmeter?

4. What problem could cause a circuit breaker to offer 40 Ω of resistance when it was in the closed position?

5. What ohmmeter readings would be expected if the circuit breaker contacts had been melted together so that they would not open?

A fuse can be tested with a voltmeter or a multimeter set to measure voltage.

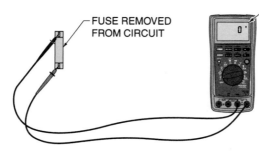

6. What voltage reading would be expected from a good fuse?

7. What voltage reading would be expected from a bad fuse?

A fuse can be tested with an ohmmeter or a multimeter set to measure resistance.

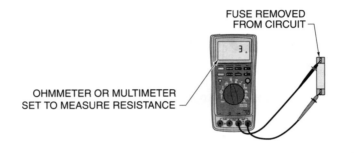

FUSE REMOVED FROM CIRCUIT

OHMMETER OR MULTIMETER SET TO MEASURE RESISTANCE

8. What resistance reading would be expected from a good fuse?

9. What resistance reading would be expected from a bad fuse?

10. What ohmmeter reading would be expected from a good time delay fuse?

Activity 4-10. Testing Transformers

The primary and secondary coils of a transformer are tested with voltmeters or multimeters set to measure voltage.

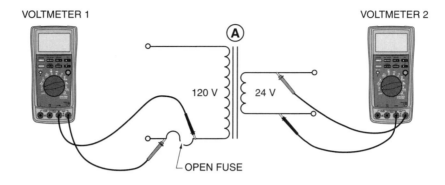

VOLTMETER 1

VOLTMETER 2

A

120 V   24 V

OPEN FUSE

1. What will Voltmeter 1 read for the fuse in Transformer A?

2. What would Voltmeter 1 read if the fuse in the transformer is good?

3. What will Voltmeter 2 read for Transformer A with the blown fuse?

4. What would Voltmeter 2 read if the fuse in the transformer is good?

The primary or secondary coils of several transformers are tested with ohmmeters or multimeters set to measure resistance.

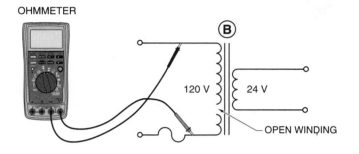

5. What will the ohmmeter read for Transformer B?

6. What would the ohmmeter read for a good transformer?

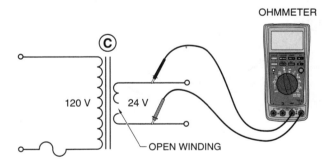

7. What will the ohmmeter read for Transformer C?

8. What would the ohmmeter read for a good transformer?

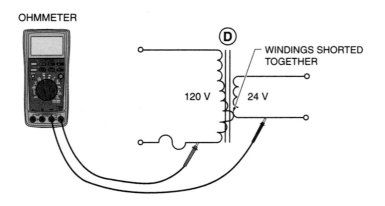

9. What will the ohmmeter read for Transformer D?

10. What would the ohmmeter read for a good transformer?

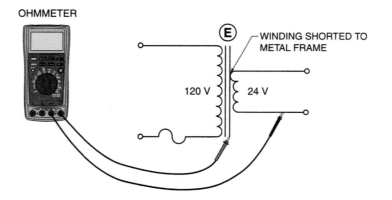

11. What will the ohmmeter read for Transformer E?

12. What would the ohmmeter read for a good transformer?

13. Are transformers repairable?

14. After a transformer has been damaged by overheating, what can be done to prevent the problem from recurring on the replacement transformer?

Activity 4-11. Testing Coils

When a coil is damaged and develops a short circuit, it usually burns open quickly from the overheating. A voltmeter or multimeter set to measure voltage can be used to detect open coils.

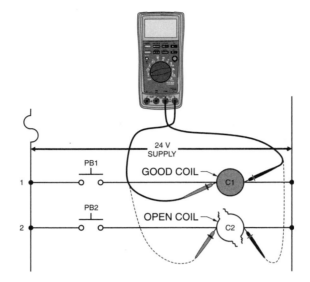

1. What voltage reading would be expected across C1 when PB1 is open?

2. What voltage reading would be expected across C1 when PB1 is closed?

3. What voltage reading would be expected across C2 when PB2 is open?

4. What voltage reading would be expected across C2 when PB2 is closed?

5. What resistance reading would be expected from a good coil?

6. What resistance reading would be expected from an open coil?

Activity 4-12. Testing Three-Phase Motors

Before a three-phase motor is replaced, it should be tested to determine if the motor coils are open, shorted together, or shorted to the metal frame of the motor. An ohmmeter or a multimeter set to measure resistance is connected to test each of the motor's coils. Possible readings are no resistance, some resistance, or overload (OL).

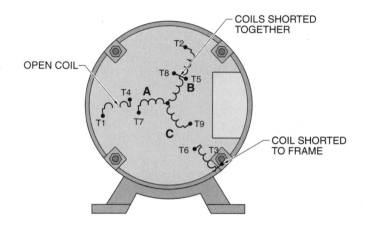

1. What is the resistance between T1 and T4?

2. What is the resistance between T2 and T5?

3. What is the resistance between T3 and T6?

4. What is the resistance between T7 and T9?

5. What is the resistance between T4 and frame?

6. What is the resistance between T5 and frame?

7. What is the resistance between T6 and frame?

8. What is the resistance between T7 and frame?

9. What is the resistance between T1 and T2?

10. What is the resistance between T1 and T6?

11. What is the resistance between T1 and T7?

12. What is the resistance between T2 and T3?

13. What is the resistance between T2 and T7?

Name _____   Date _____

Industrial Maintenance

_____   **1.** A(n) ___ device is an electronic component that switches or controls the flow of current in a circuit with no moving parts.

_____   **2.** A(n) ___ board is a thin plate of insulating material, such as fiberglass or phenolic, with conducting paths laminated to one or both sides.

_____   **3.** ___ voltage is temporary, undesirable voltage spike, ranging from a few volts to several thousand volts and lasting a few microseconds up to several milliseconds.
  - A. Transverse
  - B. Transient
  - C. Transparent
  - D. Translucent

_____   **4.** A voltage sag is a ___ decrease below the normal rated line voltage.
  - A. 0% – 5%
  - B. 5% – 10%
  - C. 10%+
  - D. none of the above

T F   **5.** A PC board must be handled under static-free conditions only.

T F   **6.** The fundamental line frequency in the U.S. is 60 Hz.

T F   **7.** Diodes are marked or shaped to indicate their anode and cathode.

_____   **8.** A(n) ___ is a diode that produces light when current flows through it.

_____   **9.** A(n) ___ is an electrical component that converts AC to DC by allowing voltage and current to move in only one direction.

_____   **10.** A(n) ___ is a three-terminal semiconductor device that controls current flow depending on the amount of voltage applied to the base.

_____   **11.** A(n) ___ is an electrical switch that is actuated by a separate circuit.

_____   **12.** ___ current is the small amount of current flowing through a solid-state device when it is not conducting.

_____   **13.** A(n) ___ is a control device that uses a preset time period as a control function.

_____   **14.** A(n) ___ is a device that changes DC voltage into AC voltage of any frequency.

_____   **15.** A(n) ___ is a solid-state control device that is programmed and reprogrammed to automatically control an industrial process or machine.
  - A. I/O
  - B. PLC
  - C. CPU
  - D. PC

_____   **16.** A voltage swell is a ___ increase above the normal rated line voltage.
  - A. 0%
  - B. 5% – 10%
  - C. 10%+
  - D. none of the above

_____   **17.** A ___ is a material that has little resistance and permits electrons to move through it easily.
  - A. conductor
  - B. semiconductor
  - C. resistor
  - D. none of the above

75

_____ **18.** ___-type material is semiconductor material with empty spaces (holes) in its crystalline structure.
    A. P   C. PN
    B. N   D. NP

_____ **19.** ___-type material is semiconductor material with free electrons in its crystalline structure.
    A. P   C. PN
    B. N   D. NP

_____ **20.** A(n) ___ is an electronic component that allows current to pass in only one direction.

_____ **21.** A(n) ___ rectifier is a rectifier containing four diodes.
    A. half-wave   C. bridge
    B. inverting   D. none of the above

_____ **22.** A ___ sensor is a device that reacts to the proximity of a target without physical contact.
    A. manual   C. proximity
    B. physical   D. thermal

_____ **23.** A(n) ___ fault is the malfunctioning of only a section or several sections of a machine.

T   F   **24.** Computer operation cannot be adversely affected by momentary power interruptions.

T   F   **25.** Heat sinks are devices that conduct and dissipate heat away from a component.

T   F   **26.** A large percentage of electronic device failures are caused by static electricity discharges.

T   F   **27.** A half-wave rectifier is a circuit containing a diode that permits both the positive and negative halves of the AC sine wave to pass.

_____ **28.** ___ current is the minimum current required to keep an SCR conducting.

_____ **29.** A(n) ___ is a device that combines the effect of a photodiode and the switching capability of a transistor.

_____ **30.** A ___ is a device that produces electricity when two different metals that are joined together are heated.
    A. thermistor   C. triac
    B. transducer   D. thermocouple

Isolated Receptacle Grounding

_____ **1.** Neutral conductor

_____ **2.** Hot conductor

_____ **3.** Isolated ground conductor

_____ **4.** Building ground for conduit and other equipment

_____ **5.** Identification of isolated grounded receptacles

_____ **6.** Conduit

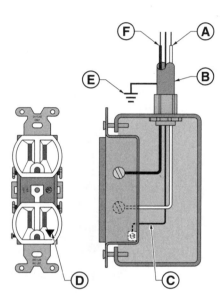

PC Boards

_____ **1.** Terminal contacts

_____ **2.** Electrical components

_____ **3.** Insulated board

_____ **4.** Pads

_____ **5.** Connector

_____ **6.** Bus

_____ **7.** Traces

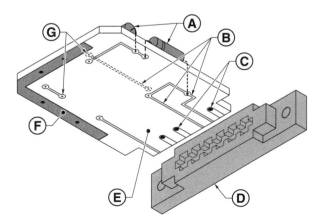

Testing Power Supplies

_____ **1.** Measure power supply output

_____ **2.** Measure transformer primary and secondary voltage

_____ **3.** Measure power supply fuse

_____ **4.** Measure voltage source

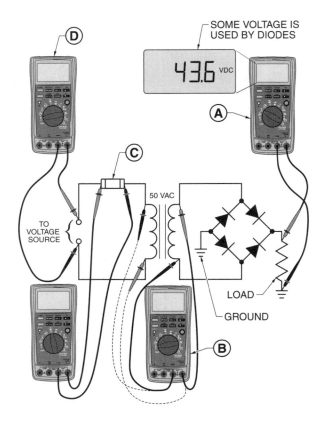

Name _____   **Date** _____

Activity 5-1. Mechanical and Electronic Contacts

Mechanical and/or electronic contacts are used in various circuits to switch loads.

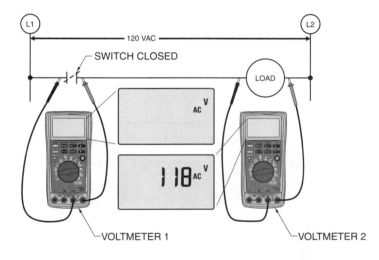

1. How much voltage drop should Voltmeter 1 read across the closed mechanical contact?

2. Is the voltage drop to the load that is indicated by Voltmeter 2 within specifications?

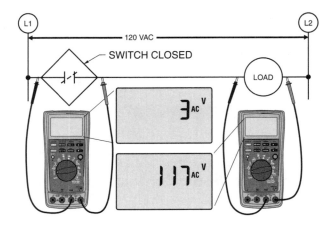

3. Why is there a 3 V drop across this electronic contact in the closed position?

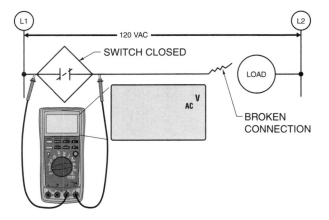

4. How much voltage drop would be indicated across the electronic contact?

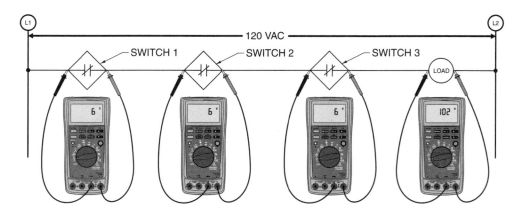

5. Would this load operate properly?

Activity 5-2. Testing Diodes

A power supply with a diode is obviously damaged. There are signs of overheating and the diode is cracked. The diode is a solder-on type.

1. Why is it unlikely that the diode would be replaced by soldering in the field?

2. What three conditions could cause the diode to fail?

Several other diodes on the power supply are tested with a digital multimeter. The first reading tests the diode in forward bias and the second reading tests the diode in reverse bias.

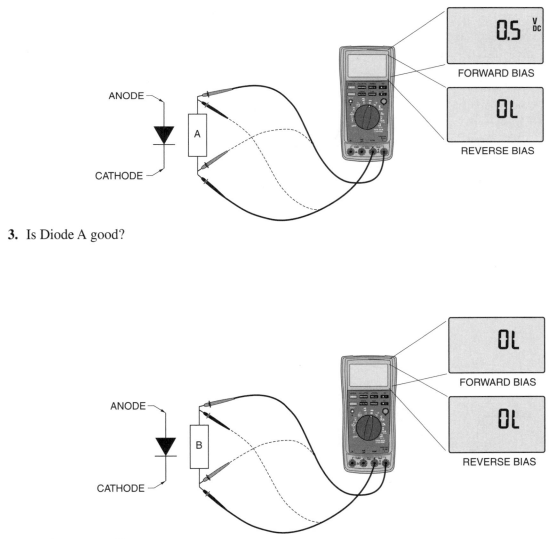

3. Is Diode A good?

4. Is Diode B good?

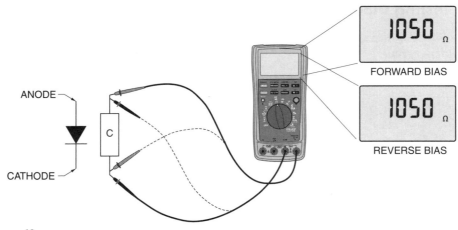

ANODE

CATHODE

C

1050 Ω

FORWARD BIAS

1050 Ω

REVERSE BIAS

5. Is Diode C good?

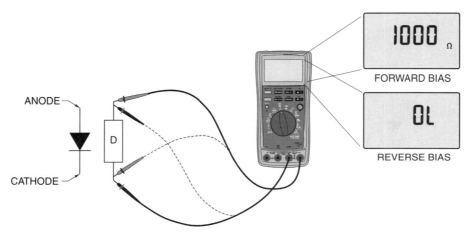

ANODE

CATHODE

D

1000 Ω

FORWARD BIAS

OL

REVERSE BIAS

6. Is Diode D good?

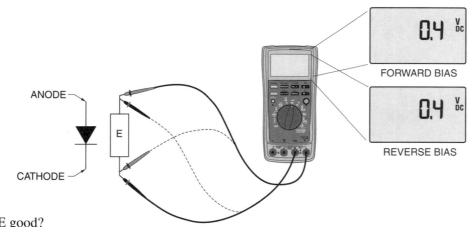

ANODE

CATHODE

E

0.4 V_{DC}

FORWARD BIAS

0.4 V_{DC}

REVERSE BIAS

7. Is Diode E good?

Activity 5-3. Testing Thermistors

Thermistors change resistance in response to a change in temperature. Thermistors are tested by measuring their resistance (or current) with a multimeter.

1. When testing a thermistor, what technical information is needed?

At 85°F, Thermistors A and B should have a resistance of 25 Ω ±2%.

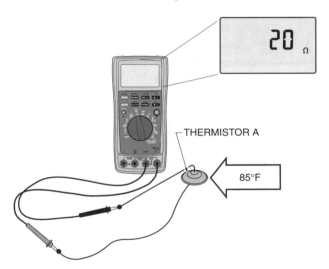

2. Is Thermistor A good?

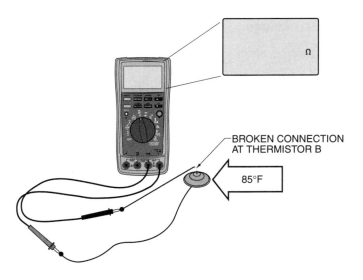

BROKEN CONNECTION
AT THERMISTOR B

85°F

3. What will Thermistor B read?

At 75°F, Thermistor C should have a resistance of 50 Ω ±2%. At 100°F, it should have a resistance of 25 Ω ±2%.

4. Will the current flowing through Thermistor C go up or down when temperature increases?

5. What four conditions could cause a thermistor to fail?

Activity 5-4. Testing Thermocouples

Thermocouples produce small amounts of electricity when heated. The voltage varies in response to the temperature. Thermocouples are tested by measuring their voltage with a multimeter. At 75°F, Thermocouples A and B should generate 25 mVDC ±2%.

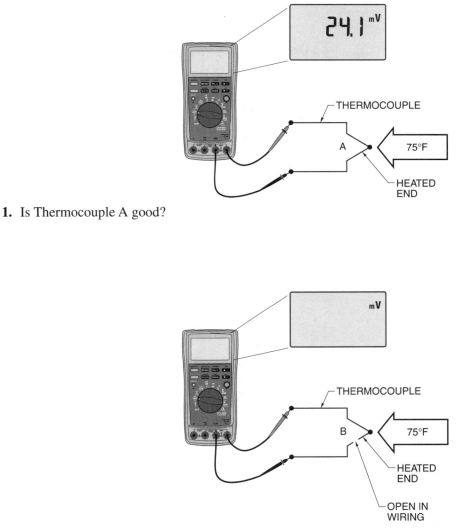

1. Is Thermocouple A good?

2. How much voltage will Thermocouple B indicate?

3. What would Thermocouple B read if tested by an ohmmeter?

4. Should a good thermocouple read any resistance if tested by an ohmmeter?

At 75°F, Thermocouples C and D should generate 25 mVDC ±2%. At 100°F, Thermocouples C and D should generate 50 mVDC ±2%.

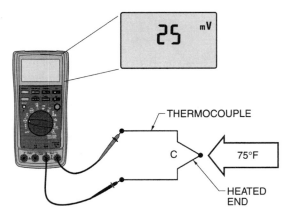

5. Is Thermocouple C good?

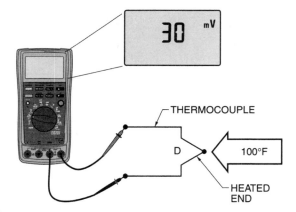

6. Is Thermocouple D good?

7. How can inventory management help minimize downtime when working on equipment controlled by thermocouples?

8. What might happen if a damaged thermocouple in a piece of equipment was replaced with one with different specifications?

A piece of equipment is controlled by a system including a thermocouple. The thermocouple's connection wires are loose.

9. What might happen to the signal from the thermocouple?

10. How might this affect the operation of the equipment?

Activity 5-5. PLC Troubleshooting

A control circuit uses switches (S1–S6) to activate loads (L1–L4) based on the logic programmed into a PLC. This logic is shown in both a line diagram and a PLC program diagram. The switches and loads are currently in their normal states.

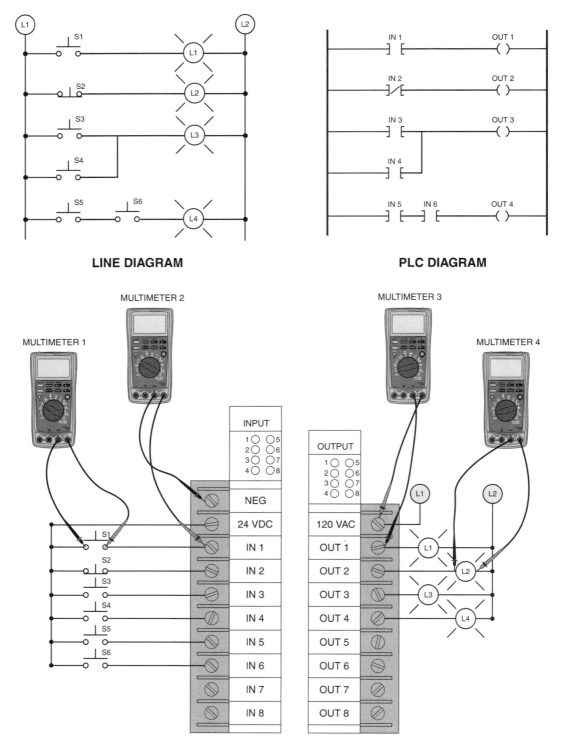

LINE DIAGRAM

PLC DIAGRAM

1. Which input and output indicator light(s) should be illuminated?

2. What reading should Multimeter 1 indicate?

3. What reading should Multimeter 2 indicate?

4. What reading should Multimeter 3 indicate?

5. What reading should Multimeter 4 indicate?

Switch 1 (S1) is now activated.

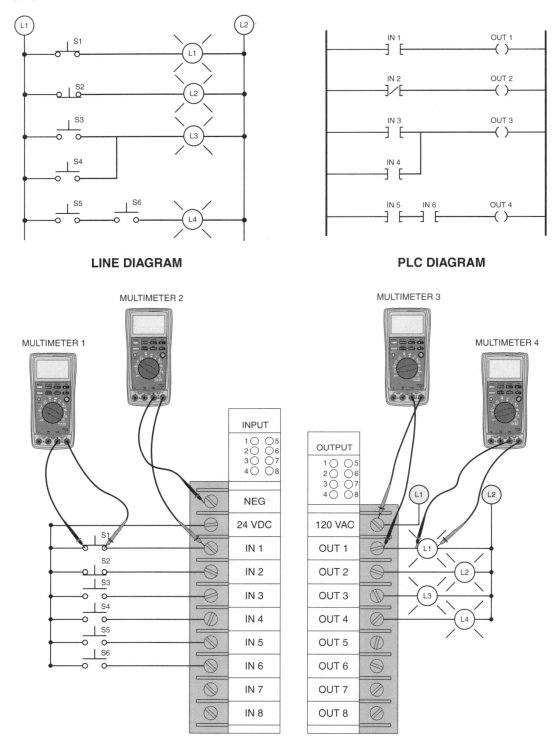

LINE DIAGRAM

PLC DIAGRAM

6. Which input and output indicator light(s) should be illuminated?

7. What reading should Multimeter 1 indicate?

8. What reading should Multimeter 2 indicate?

9. What reading should Multimeter 3 indicate?

10. What reading should Multimeter 4 indicate?

Switch 1 (S1) is deactivated and Switch 2 (S2) is activated.

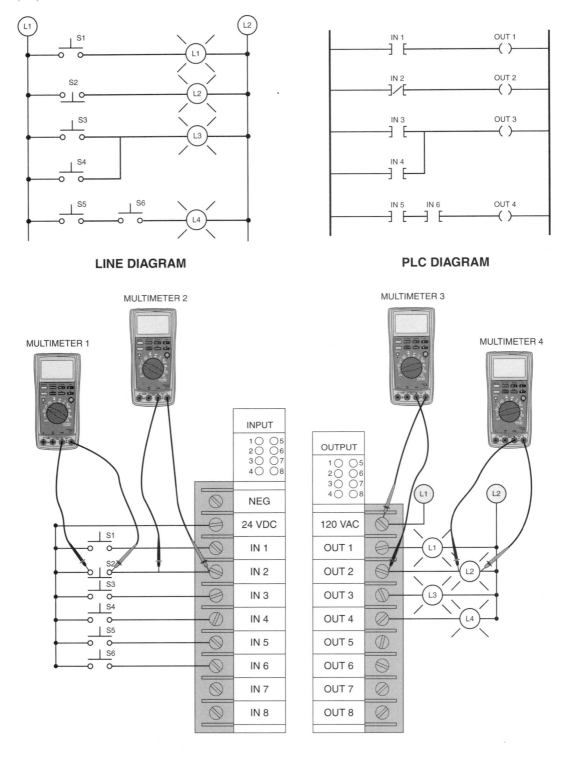

LINE DIAGRAM

PLC DIAGRAM

11. Which input and output indicator light(s) should be illuminated?

12. What reading should Multimeter 1 indicate?

13. What reading should Multimeter 2 indicate?

14. What reading should Multimeter 3 indicate?

15. What reading should Multimeter 4 indicate?

Switch 2 (S2) is deactivated and Switch 3 (S3) is activated.

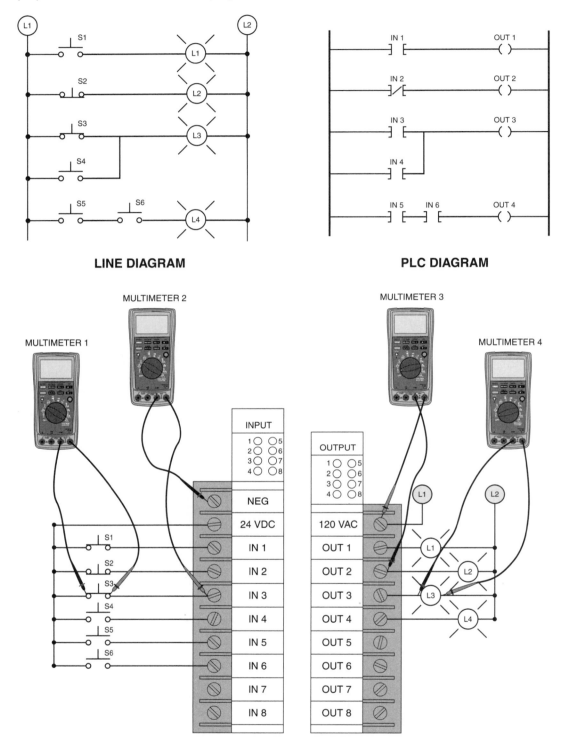

LINE DIAGRAM

PLC DIAGRAM

16. Which input and output indicator light(s) should be illuminated?

17. What reading should Multimeter 1 indicate?

18. What reading should Multimeter 2 indicate?

19. What reading should Multimeter 3 indicate?

20. What reading should Multimeter 4 indicate?

Name _____   Date _____

Industrial Maintenance

_____ 1. A(n) ___ is a chemical substance that vaporizes (boils) at a low temperature.

_____ 2. ___ heat is heat energy that can be measured by a change in temperature.

_____ 3. Change of ___ is the process that occurs when enough heat is added to or removed from a substance to change it from one physical state to another.

_____ 4. A(n) ___ is a heat exchanger through which heat is transferred to the low-pressure refrigerant liquid.
    A. compressor   C. evaporator
    B. condenser   D. none of the above

_____ 5. A(n) ___ is a temperature sensor inside a temperature-controlled space that sends signals to a control system in order to maintain a set temperature.

T   F   6. Refrigeration systems are designed to maintain a specific temperature rather than a range of temperatures.

T   F   7. Heat flows only from a warmer temperature to a cooler temperature.

_____ 8. A(n) ___ pump is a mechanical compression refrigeration system that can reverse the flow of refrigerant, switching between heating and cooling modes.

_____ 9. ___ is the cooling of a substance to a temperature that is lower than its saturation temperature at a particular pressure.

_____ 10. ___ condensers are the most common condensers used in refrigeration systems.
    A. Air-cooled   C. Evaporative
    B. Water-cooled   D. none of the above

_____ 11. An automatic ___ valve is a valve that is opened and closed by the pressure in the line ahead of the valve.

_____ 12. ___ is the temperature below which moisture in the air begins to condense.

_____ 13. The ___ is the difference between the cut-out pressure and cut-in pressure of a compressor.

T   F   14. Heat pumps are classified as air-to-air, water-to-water, or air-to-water.

T   F   15. Charging is adding refrigerant to a system.

_____ 16. A(n) ___ device is a component that controls the flow rate of refrigerant into an evaporator.

_____ 17. ___ temperature is the temperature at which a refrigerant changes state by vaporizing or condensing.

T   F   18. All substances exist in either a solid, liquid, or gaseous state.

_____ 19. ___ is capable of moving much more heat per pound of liquid vaporized than other refrigerants.

T   F   20. High-pressure refrigerant can freeze the eyes and skin.

_____ **21.** ___ is a measurement of the intensity of heat.

_____ **22.** ___ heat is heat energy that causes a change of state but no temperature change.

_____ **23.** A(n) ___ is a heat exchanger that removes heat from high-pressure refrigerant vapor.

_____ **24.** A ___ compressor is a compressor that is completely sealed inside a welded case.
   A. heritable   C. hermetic
   B. hemic   D. none of the above

_____ **25.** Compressor ___ occurs when the compressor motor overheats, melting the motor insulation.

_____ **26.** ___ is sensible heat added to a substance after it has turned to vapor.

_____ **27.** ___ humidity is the amount of moisture in the air compared to the amount of moisture the air would hold if it were saturated.

_____ **28.** A(n) ___ valve is a valve that removes unwanted gases from the system.

_____ **29.** Refrigerant ___ is the process of removing refrigerant from a system and capturing it in a recovery cylinder, with no cleaning of the refrigerant.
   A. recovery   C. reclaiming
   B. recycling   D. all of the above

_____ **30.** A deep vacuum for refrigerant evacuation is a vacuum between ___.
   A. 4 μm and 70 μm   C. 400 μm and 700 μm
   B. 40 μm and 700 μm   D. none of the above

_____ **31.** A(n) ___ point is a point in a refrigeration system where there is a significant pressure change.

T   F   **32.** Refrigerants used in modern refrigeration systems are derived from methane or ethane.

_____ **33.** ___ is the process of varying the amount of refrigerant pumped by a compressor.

T   F   **34.** A micron is a unit of measure equal to one-millionth of an inch.

T   F   **35.** An electronic leak detector may give an audible tone or a visual signal when the detector senses refrigerant.

_____ **36.** ___ is a form of energy identified by a temperature difference between objects or a change of state.

_____ **37.** Saturated liquid is liquid at a certain pressure and temperature that vaporizes if the temperature ___.

T   F   **38.** Adding heat increases the energy content of a substance.

_____ **39.** A(n) ___ comb is a device used to straighten the edges of the thin metal that extend from a condenser or evaporator coil.

T   F   **40.** Liquids cannot be compressed.

Heat Pumps — Heating Mode

_____ 1. Compressor

_____ 2. Indoor coil

_____ 3. Outdoor coil

_____ 4. Heat to heated space

_____ 5. Heat from outside

_____ 6. Refrigerant flow

_____ 7. Expansion device

_____ 8. Spool

_____ 9. Reversing valve

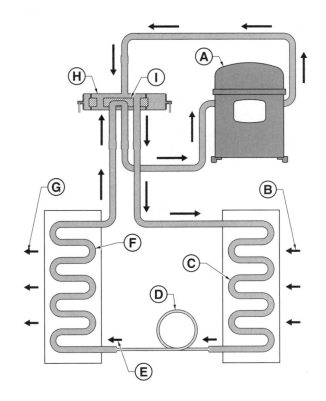

Hot-Gas Defrost

_____ 1. Condenser

_____ 2. Sight glass

_____ 3. Compressor

_____ 4. Evaporator

_____ 5. Reevaporator

_____ 6. Reevaporator fan

_____ 7. Accumulator

_____ 8. Timer

_____ 9. Bypass solenoids

_____ 10. Filter-dryer

_____ 11. Defrost heater

_____ 12. Metering device

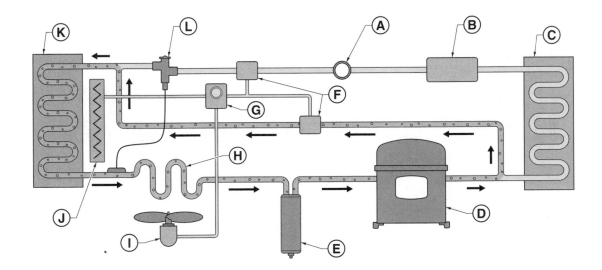

Cooling Towers

_____   **1.** Cooling tower

_____   **2.** Condenser

_____   **3.** Tiles

_____   **4.** Cool refrigerant out

_____   **5.** Cool water in

_____   **6.** Cool dry air in

_____   **7.** Warm moist air out

_____   **8.** Warm water out

_____   **9.** Hot refrigerant in

_____   **10.** Condenser tubes

_____   **11.** Water pump

_____   **12.** Makeup water inlet

_____   **13.** Warm condenser water spray

_____   **14.** Fan

_____   **15.** Moisture eliminators

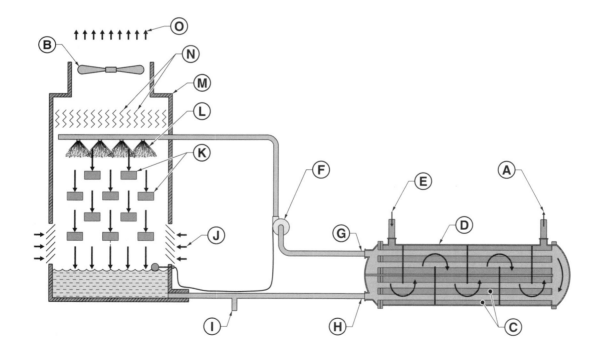

Ammonia Refrigeration Systems

_____   **1.** Condenser

_____   **2.** Receiver

_____   **3.** Evaporator

_____   **4.** Compressor

_____   **5.** Roof diffuser

_____   **6.** Emergency relief valve

_____   **7.** Relief valves

_____   **8.** Isolation valves

_____   **9.** Condensing water

_____   **10.** Purge valves

_____   **11.** Secondary coolant

_____   **12.** Oil separator

_____   **13.** Metering device

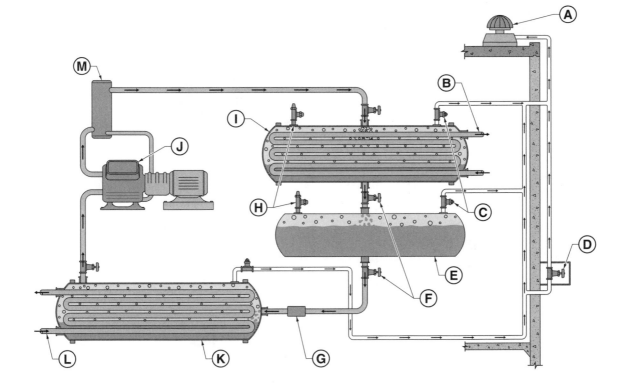

Mechanical Compression Refrigeration System

_____ 1. Evaporator
_____ 2. Compressor
_____ 3. Condenser
_____ 4. Cold air to cooled space
_____ 5. Hot air
_____ 6. Warm air from cooled space
_____ 7. Warm outside air

_____ 8. Vaporizing refrigerant
_____ 9. Condensing refrigerant
_____ 10. Liquid refrigerant
_____ 11. Refrigerant vapor
_____ 12. Filter-drier
_____ 13. Sight glass
_____ 14. Metering device

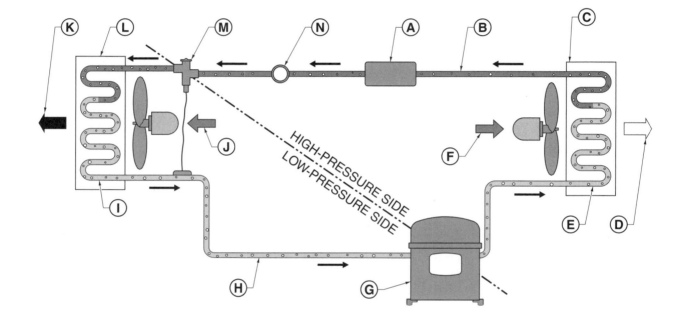

Compressors

_____ 1. Vane
_____ 2. Screw
_____ 3. Reciprocating
_____ 4. Centrifugal

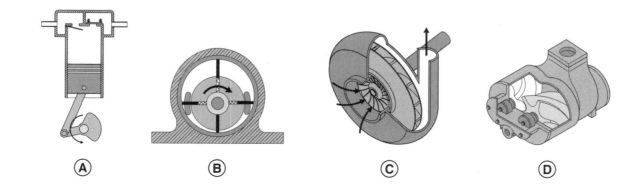

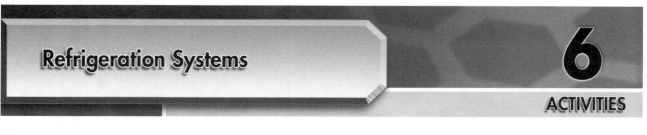

Refrigeration Systems

6

ACTIVITIES

Name _____   Date _____

Activity 6-1. Refrigerant States

Complete the drawing of the refrigeration system.

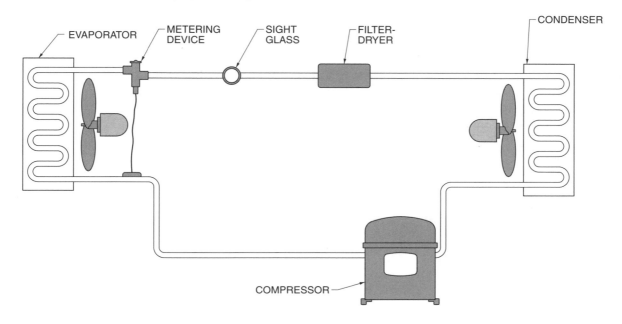

1. Indicate the direction of refrigerant flow with arrows.

2. Sketch in the state of the refrigerant as it travels through the system. Use solid shading to indicate liquid refrigerant, light shading with bubbles to indicate vaporizing refrigerant, and no shading to indicate refrigerant vapor.

3. Sketch a line to separate the high-pressure and low-pressure sides.

4. Write in the state of the refrigerant in various parts of the system using the words "vaporizing," "condensing," "subcooled," and "superheated."

5. Indicate the direction of airflow through the evaporator using large arrows and label them with the relative temperature of the air entering and leaving the evaporator. For example, label arrows with "hot air," "warm air," "cool air," or "cold air."

6. Indicate the direction of airflow through the condenser using large arrows and label them with the relative temperature of the air entering and leaving the condenser. For example, label arrows with "hot air," "warm air," "cool air," or "cold air."

7. Why does a refrigeration system need a low-pressure and a high-pressure side to move heat into the evaporator and out of the condenser?

Activity 6-2. Temperature-Pressure Charts

Most refrigerants have an exact pressure-temperature relationship. At a given pressure, there will be only one saturation temperature, the temperature at which the refrigerant will vaporize or condense. This relationship is shown in temperature-pressure charts.

REFRIGERANT VAPOR PRESSURE*			
Temp†	HCFC-22	HCFC-123	HFC-134a
−180	—	—	—
−170	—	—	—
−160	—	—	—
−150	29.4‡	—	—
−140	29.0‡	—	—
−130	28.5‡	—	—
−120	27.7‡	—	—
−110	26.6‡	—	—
−100	25.0‡	—	28.1‡
−90	23.0‡	—	27.1‡
−80	20.2‡	—	25.9‡
−70	16.6‡	—	24.1‡
−60	12.0‡	29.4‡	21.8‡
−50	6.1‡	29.1‡	18.7‡
−40	0.5	28.8‡	14.8‡
−30	4.9	28.3‡	9.9‡
−20	10.2	27.7‡	3.7‡
−10	16.5	26.9‡	1.9
0	24.0	25.8‡	6.5
10	32.8	24.5‡	11.9
20	43.0	22.8‡	18.4
30	54.9	20.7‡	26.1
40	68.4	18.1‡	35.1
50	83.9	15.0‡	45.5
60	101.4	11.2‡	57.5
70	121.2	6.6‡	71.2
80	143.3	1.3‡	86.8
90	168.0	2.5	104.4
100	195.4	6.1	124.3
110	225.8	10.3	146.5
120	259.3	15.1	171.3
130	296.1	20.6	198.9
140	336.5	26.8	229.4
150	380.8	33.9	263.0
160	429.2	41.8	300.1
170	482.0	50.6	340.8
180	539.4	60.4	385.6
190	602.1	71.3	434.7
200	670.3	83.4	488.7
210	—	96.6	548.3

* in psi
† in °F
‡ in inches of mercury vacuum

1. What is the saturation temperature of HCFC-22 at 32.8 psi?

2. What is the saturation temperature of HCFC-22 at 143.3 psi?

3. If 17°F air is blowing over an evaporator coil that contains HCFC-22 at 33 psi, will the refrigerant vaporize?

4. If 80°F air is blowing over a condenser coil that contains HCFC-22 at 226 psi, will the refrigerant condense?

5. What is the saturation pressure of HCFC-22 at 40°F?

6. What is the saturation pressure of HCFC-22 at 140°F?

7. What is the saturation temperature of HCFC-123 at 28.3 in. Hg vacuum?

8. What is the saturation temperature of HCFC-123 at 10.3 psi?

9. If the temperature is 50°F, will the refrigerant in an open container of HCFC-123 vaporize if the container is at sea level?

10. What is the saturation temperature of HFC-134a at 11.9 psi?

11. What is the saturation temperature of HFC-134a at 198.9 psi?

A technician takes temperature and pressure readings on a container of refrigerant recovered from several systems. The pressure is 50 psi over what is expected according to the type of refrigerant and the temperature of the container.

12. What is the most likely cause of the unexpected reading?

13. Should this refrigerant be used in a system?

14. If not, what should be done with this refrigerant?

Activity 6-3. Compressors

A reciprocating compressor in a refrigeration system has clogged valves that do not seal properly.

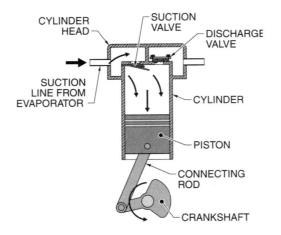

1. What could happen to the low-pressure side and high-pressure side system pressures?

2. What would likely happen to the temperature in the cooled space?

3. How could this problem cause the compressor to overheat?

4. What maintenance do hermetic compressors require?

5. List two common maintenance activities for large, serviceable compressors.

Activity 6-4. Condensers

Complete the drawing of the normally operating refrigeration condenser. The temperature inside the condenser should be about 35°F higher than the air blowing through the condenser coils. The outside air temperature is 85°F. The refrigerant is HFC-22.

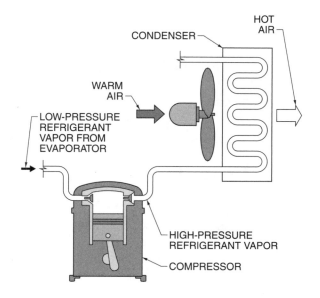

1. Sketch in the state of the refrigerant as it travels through the condenser. Use solid shading to indicate liquid refrigerant, light shading with bubbles to indicate vaporizing refrigerant, and no shading to indicate refrigerant vapor.

2. What is the expected pressure inside the condenser?

3. Why should the condenser temperature be so much higher than the surrounding air?

Another condenser under the same operating conditions has coils and fins that are dirty and bent.

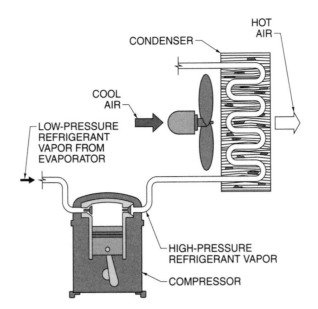

4. Sketch in the state of the refrigerant as it travels through the condenser. Use solid shading to indicate liquid refrigerant, light shading with bubbles to indicate vaporizing refrigerant, and no shading to indicate refrigerant vapor.

5. Why would the subcooling in this condenser be low?

6. What problem could occur in an evaporator if the air temperature cooling the condenser was very cold?

7. List two common maintenance activities for air-cooled condensers.

The condenser fan in a separate refrigeration system is not operating.

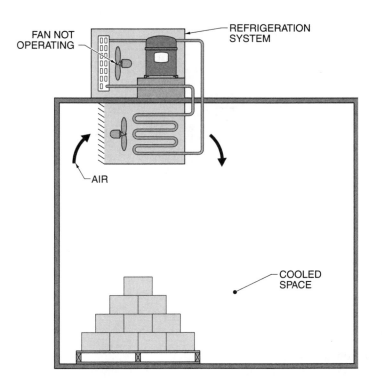

8. What three symptoms could develop from this problem?

9. Could a refrigerant gauge manifold be used to diagnose this problem?

10. What are three possible causes of this problem?

11. Which other component might have been damaged because of this problem?

Activity 6-5. Evaporators

Refrigerant HFC-22 travels through a normally operating evaporator cooling a space to 30°F. The refrigerant enters the evaporator at a temperature of 20°F and is superheated by 10°F. The inside of the evaporator should be at least 10°F cooler than the air flowing across the evaporator coils.

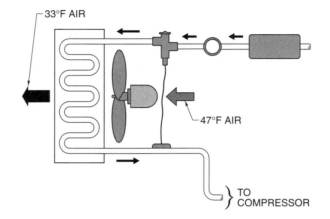

1. Sketch the state of the refrigerant as it travels through the evaporator. Use solid shading to indicate liquid refrigerant, light shading with bubbles to indicate vaporizing refrigerant, and no shading to indicate refrigerant vapor.

2. What is the temperature of the refrigerant at the inlet of the evaporator?

3. What is the expected temperature of the refrigerant at the outlet of the evaporator?

4. Why should the temperature of the evaporator be so much lower than the surrounding air?

5. What is the pressure in this evaporator?

6. List three common maintenance activities to aid proper airflow through an evaporator.

The refrigerant travels through a starved evaporator. The refrigerant enters the evaporator at a temperature of 20°F and leaves at 40°F.

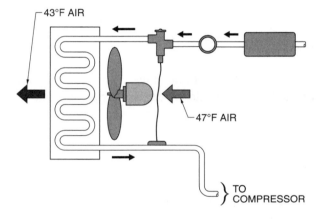

7. Sketch the state of the refrigerant as it travels through the evaporator. Use solid shading to indicate liquid refrigerant, light shading with bubbles to indicate vaporizing refrigerant, and no shading to indicate refrigerant vapor.

8. What two symptoms could develop from this situation?

9. What are two possible causes of this problem?

The refrigerant travels through a flooded evaporator. The refrigerant enters the evaporator at a temperature of 20°F.

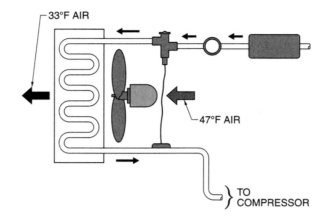

10. Sketch the state of the refrigerant as it travels through the evaporator. Use solid shading to indicate liquid refrigerant, light shading with bubbles to indicate vaporizing refrigerant, and no shading to indicate refrigerant vapor.

11. What two symptoms could develop from this situation?

12. What are two possible causes of this problem?

An evaporator equipped with an automatic defrost cycle is found covered with thick ice.

13. What are two possible causes of this problem?

A cooled space is not at the correct temperature but the evaporator is very cold.

14. What is the most likely cause of this problem?

15. Why might the evaporator ice up because of this problem?

16. Why might the suction piping leading to the compressor be sweating or frosted?

Activity 6-6. Hot-Gas Defrost

A refrigeration system is set up for hot-gas defrost.

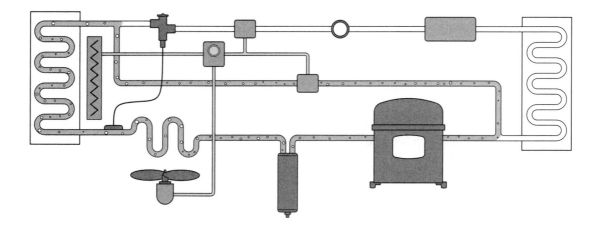

1. Indicate the direction of refrigerant flow with arrows.

2. Which electrical components are energized during hot-gas defrost?

3. If the bypass solenoid valve failed, what would happen when the timer called for the defrost cycle to begin?

4. If the bypass system was operating correctly but not all the frost was melting during defrosting, what is the likely cause of this problem?

5. What is the purpose of the accumulator in the hot-gas defrost system?

6. List common maintenance activities for a hot-gas defrost system?

Activity 6-7. Temperature Control

Boxes in a cooled space are placed directly on the floor and stacked up to the bottom of the refrigeration unit.

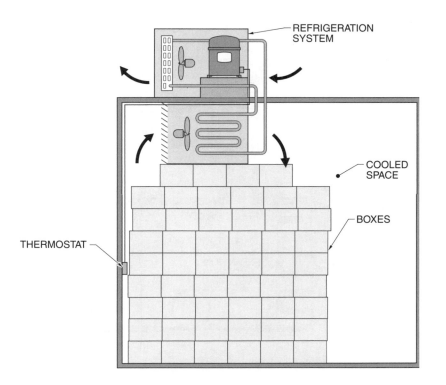

1. What three symptoms could develop from this situation?

2. Why should the boxes have been stacked on pallets instead?

3. Why should pressure readings be taken only after a few hours has passed since the cooled-space doors have been open for a long time?

Activity 6-8. Heat Pumps

A heat pump system is set up for cooling mode.

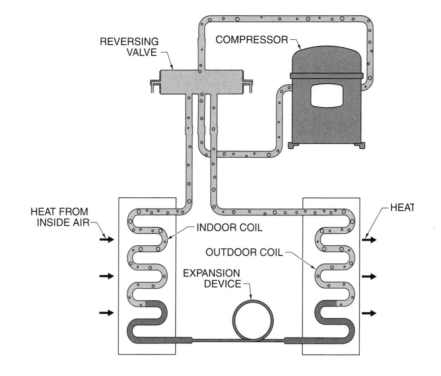

1. Sketch the spool position in the reversing valve.

2. Indicate the direction of refrigerant flow and airflow through the indoor and outdoor coils with arrows.

3. Label each coil with its current function as a "condenser" or an "evaporator."

A heat pump system is set up for heating mode.

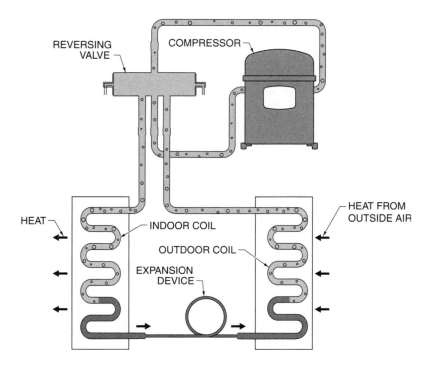

4. Sketch the spool position in the reversing valve.

5. Indicate the direction of refrigerant flow and airflow through the indoor and outdoor coils with arrows.

6. Label each coil with its current function as a "condenser" or an "evaporator."

7. Failure of which component could cause the heat pump to inadvertently switch from cooling to heating?

Activity 6-9. Chilled Water Systems

A low-pressure chilled water system is operating in a large building.

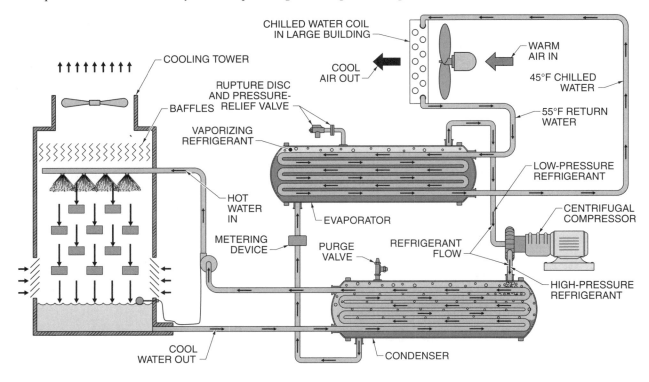

1. Do evaporators in a low-pressure chiller operate above or below atmospheric pressure?

2. What is a common pressure in the condenser?

3. What is a common setting for the rupture disc?

4. Which device prevents all the refrigerant from escaping the system if the rupture disc bursts?

5. What would happen to the system if the circulating pump sending water to the cooling tower failed?

Activity 6-10. Cooling Towers

A cooling tower is operating as part of a refrigeration system.

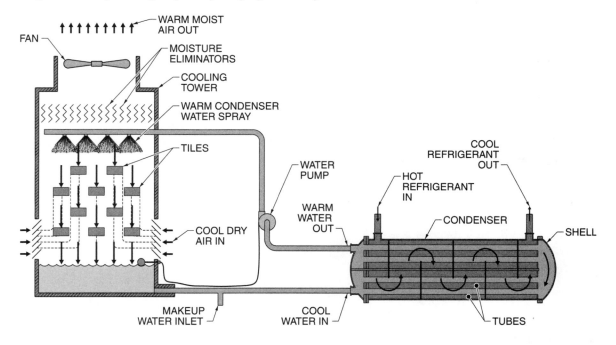

1. If the water flow to the water-cooled condenser was restricted, what would happen to the ability of the system to cool the cooled space?

2. What are two possible causes of restricted water flow?

3. What would happen to the temperature of the condenser if water flow were restricted?

4. What would happen to the temperature difference between the water entering and leaving the condenser if water flow were restricted?

5. List two common maintenance activities for water-cooled condensers.

6. List two common maintenance activities for cooling towers.

Activity 6-11. Taking Pressure Readings

A gauge manifold is set up to take pressure readings on a refrigeration system.

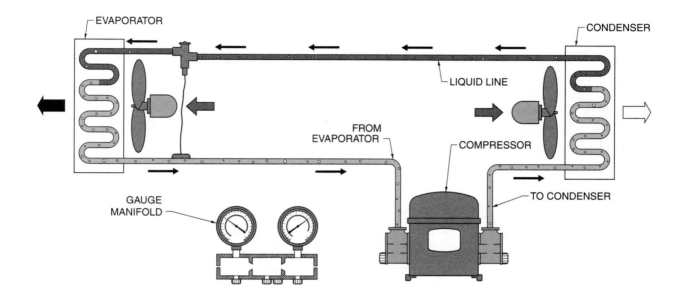

1. Sketch and label the valve positions on the service manifold and on the compressor service valves.

2. Sketch the hose connections.

3. How is the liquid refrigerant removed from the high-pressure side hose after taking the system pressures?

4. What are two possible causes of a small pressure difference between the high-pressure and low-pressure sides?

5. What are two possible causes of an extremely high compressor discharge-side pressure and extremely low suction-side pressure?

6. What pressures would be expected between the high-pressure and low-pressure side in a system that had not been operating for a long time?

Activity 6-12. Evacuating Systems

A gauge manifold is set up to evacuate a refrigeration system.

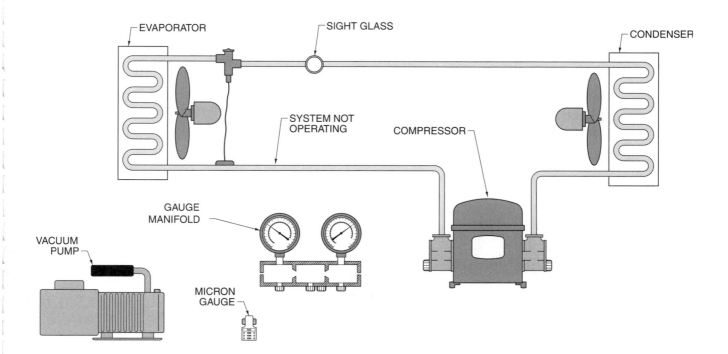

1. Sketch and label the valve positions on the service manifold and on the compressor service valves.

2. Sketch the hose connections between all the evacuation equipment.

3. What pressure level indicates that the system is evacuated?

4. What happens to the micron gauge reading immediately after the vacuum pump is turned off?

5. If the system is leaking, what will happen to the reading on the micron gauge?

6. If the system still has water in it, what will happen to the reading on the micron gauge?

Activity 6-13. Liquid Charging Systems

A gauge manifold is set up to charge a refrigeration system with liquid.

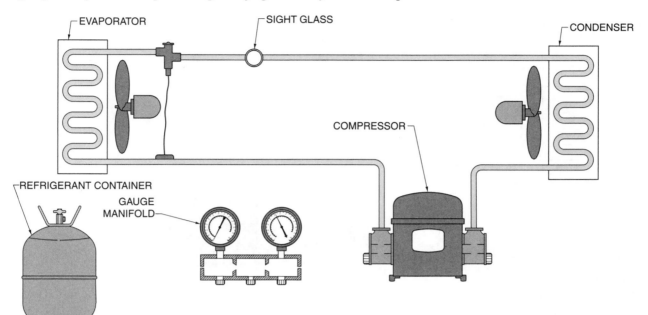

1. Sketch and label the valve positions on the service manifold and on the compressor service valves.

2. Sketch the hose connections between all the charging equipment.

3. Indicate the direction of refrigerant flow with arrows.

4. Should the container of refrigerant be right side up or upside down on the electronic scale?

5. When would liquid refrigerant stop flowing into the system?

Activity 6-14. Vapor Charging Systems

A gauge manifold is set up to charge a refrigeration system with vapor.

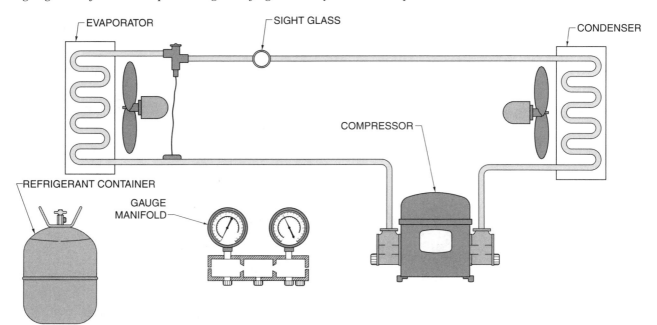

1. Sketch and label the valve positions on the service manifold and on the compressor service valves.

2. Sketch the hose connections between all the charging equipment.

3. Indicate the direction of refrigerant flow with arrows.

4. Why must the system be running while vapor charging?

5. What four conditions should be measured to determine if the system is fully charged?

Activity 6-15. Leaks

A refrigeration system has been leaking and the system is low on refrigerant.

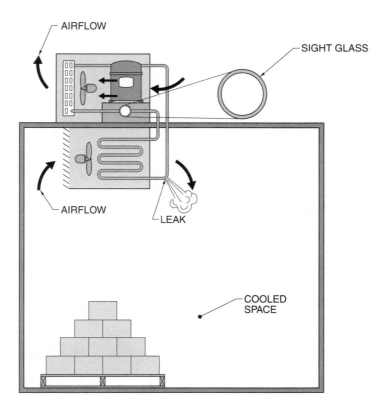

1. Sketch what will be seen in the sight glass.

2. What three symptoms could develop from this situation?

3. What are two possible causes of leaks in refrigeration systems?

4. How is a standing pressure test conducted on the system?

5. What is the technique for finding a leak with an electronic leak detector?

6. How is the general location of the leak found?

7. How is the exact location of the leak found?

8. What visual sign might be found at the site of the leak?

Name _____ **Date** _____

Industrial Maintenance

_____ **1.** ___ is water that is supplied to the boiler at the proper temperature and pressure.

_____ **2.** A(n) ___ system is a system that regulates the flow of air to and from the boiler.

_____ **3.** A(n) ___ boiler is a boiler in which the hot gases of combustion pass through tubes surrounded by water.

_____ **4.** A low-pressure boiler is a boiler that has an MAWP of up to ___ psi.
   A. 15   C. 45
   B. 30   D. 60

_____ **5.** A boiler horsepower is the power available from the evaporation of ___ lb of water per hour at a feedwater temperature of ___°F.
   A. 1; 72   C. 100; 212
   B. 34.5; 100   D. none of the above

_____ **6.** A therm is a unit of heat energy equivalent to ___ Btu.
   A. 1000   C. 100,000
   B. 10,000   D. none of the above

T   F   **7.** A package boiler is preassembled at the factory.

T   F   **8.** The ASME Code specifies the design, materials, and construction of safety valves.

_____ **9.** A(n) ___ valve is a valve that allows flow in only one direction.

_____ **10.** ___ water is water that is used to replace boiler water lost from leaks.

_____ **11.** Boilers having over ___ sq ft of boiler heating surface must have at least two means of supplying feedwater to the boiler.

_____ **12.** A(n) ___ tube is a curved, hollow tube closed on one end that straightens when steam pressure is applied in the tube.

_____ **13.** ___ combustion is combustion of all fuel using only the theoretical minimum amount of air.

_____ **14.** ___ air is air in the combustion process that regulates the rate of combustion.
   A. Primary   C. Inadequate
   B. Secondary   D. Excess

_____ **15.** Grade is a coal classification related to ___.
   A. size   C. ash content
   B. heating value   D. all of the above

_____ **16.** ___ is the difference in pressure between two points that causes air or gas to flow.

T   F   **17.** Scale acts like an insulating material and increases heat transfer efficiency, causing overheating of boiler metal.

_____ 18. A low water condition occurs when the water in a boiler is below the ___ as indicated by the gauge glass.

_____ 19. Thermal ___ is the ratio of heat absorbed to the heat available.

_____ 20. The ___ is the recommended maximum pressure at which the boiler can safely be operated.

_____ 21. ___ heat is heat that can be measured by a change in temperature.

_____ 22. ___ heat is heat energy that causes a change of state and no temperature change.
    A Potent   C. Patent
    B. Latent   D. none of the above

_____ 23. A ___ boiler is a boiler that is constructed on-site.
    A. package   C. pre-fabricated
    B. field-erected   D. none of the above

_____ 24. ___ is material that retains its strength at very high temperatures.

_____ 25. A(n) ___ valve is a fitting that prevents the boiler from exceeding its MAWP.

_____ 26. Water ___ is a banging caused by rapid water movement in steam lines.

T   F   27. Open feedwater heaters achieve higher water temperatures than closed feedwater heaters.

T   F   28. In an os&y valve, the valve is open when the stem is up.

_____ 29. A(n) ___ is a mechanical device used to feed coal pieces to a furnace.

_____ 30. A flame ___ is a safety device that senses if the pilot light and/or main flame is lit.

_____ 31. Boiler water pH should be between ___ and ___.
    A. 5; 7   C. 10; 11.5
    B. 7; 10   D. 11; 13

_____ 32. ___ lay-up is storage of a boiler with all water drained.
    A. Wet   C. Storage
    B. Dry   D. none of the above

_____ 33. The ___ steam line is a line that connects a boiler to the steam header.

_____ 34. The ___ is the lowest part of the water side of a watertube boiler and collects sludge or mud.

_____ 35. A(n) ___ valve is a valve that controls flow by raising or lowering a circular disc.

pH Scale

_____ 1. Acidic

_____ 2. Alkaline

_____ 3. Neutral

_____ 4. pH commonly required for boiler water

Mechanical Draft – Forced

_____ 1. Forced draft fan
_____ 2. Boiler drum
_____ 3. Air entering furnace
_____ 4. Gases of combustion
_____ 5. Breeching
_____ 6. Airflow
_____ 7. Furnace
_____ 8. Outlet damper
_____ 9. Inlet damper
_____ 10. Chimney

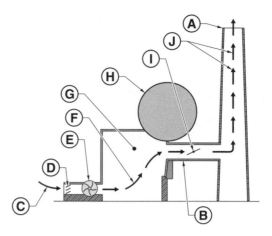

Water Columns

_____ 1. Water
_____ 2. Cross tees
_____ 3. Try cocks
_____ 4. Gauge glass blowdown valve
_____ 5. Vent
_____ 6. Top of boiler
_____ 7. Water column
_____ 8. Water level
_____ 9. Top isolation valve
_____ 10. Gauge glass
_____ 11. NOWL
_____ 12. Alarm sensor switch enclosure
_____ 13. Bottom isolation valve
_____ 14. Water column blowdown valve

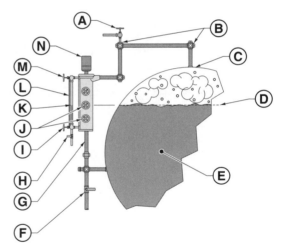

Heating Systems — Hot Water

_____ 1. Hot water flow

_____ 2. Heating unit

_____ 3. Compression tank

_____ 4. Boiler full of water

_____ 5. Branch line

_____ 6. Backflow preventer

_____ 7. Circulating pump

_____ 8. Makeup water supply line

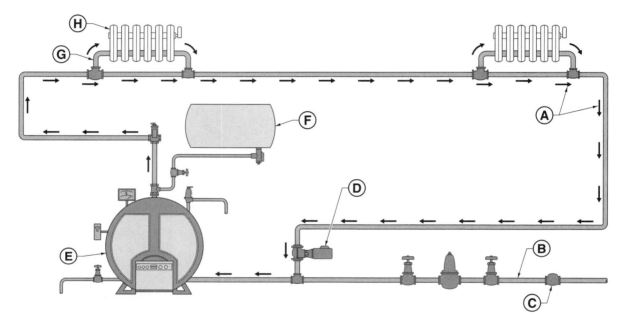

Feedwater Valves

_____ 1. Boiler

_____ 2. Feedwater pump

_____ 3. Check valves

_____ 4. Stop valves

_____ 5. Main feedwater line

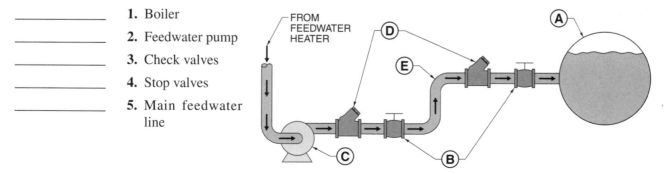

Boiler Systems

_____ 1. Draft system

_____ 2. Fuel system

_____ 3. Steam system

_____ 4. Feedwater system

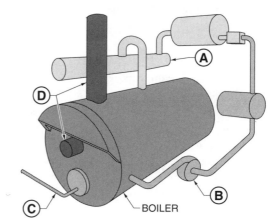

BOILER

Natural Gas Accessories

_____ 1. Pilot gas regulator

_____ 2. Coupling

_____ 3. Regulator

_____ 4. Low gas pressure switch

_____ 5. Manual pilot shutoff valve

_____ 6. Manual shutoff

_____ 7. Motorized valves

_____ 8. High gas pressure switch

_____ 9. Pilot solenoid valve

_____ 10. Vent valve

_____ 11. Butterfly valve

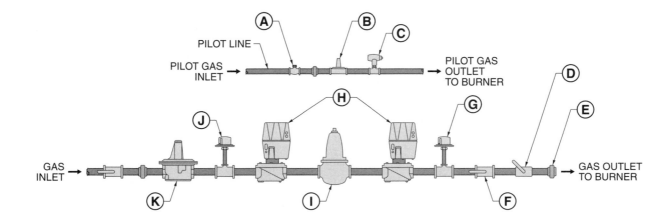

PILOT LINE

PILOT GAS INLET

PILOT GAS OUTLET TO BURNER

GAS INLET

GAS OUTLET TO BURNER

Heating Systems — Steam

_____ 1. Boiler

_____ 2. Steam flow

_____ 3. Steam trap

_____ 4. Heating unit

_____ 5. Main steam stop valve

_____ 6. Feedwater pump

_____ 7. Steam bubbles

_____ 8. Condensate flow

_____ 9. Condensate return line

_____ 10. Feedwater flow

_____ 11. Main steam line

_____ 12. Branch line

_____ 13. Steam header

_____ 14. Condensate receiver tank

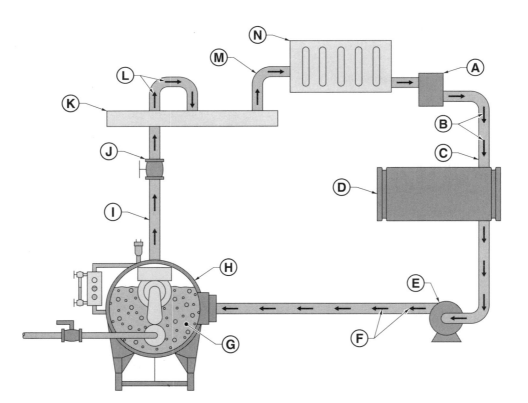

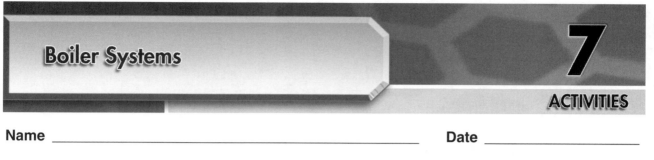

Boiler Systems

Name _____ **Date** _____

Short Answer Questions

1. Why might the AHJ lower the MAWP of the boiler?

2. Would it be legal to make a boiler designed as a low-pressure boiler into a high-pressure boiler, and what might happen if this was done?

3. What are some differences between watertube and firetube boilers?

4. If water is being forced out of the boiler through the feedwater line, which valve has failed?

5. What might happen if the vent was not opened during a boiler shutdown?

6. List all boiler components that must be locked out when the boiler is shut down and opened for its annual inspection.

7. What damage might occur if a cold boiler was started and kept on high fire?

8. Why must steam piping be warmed slowly during boiler startup?

9. Why is gas easier to burn than fuel oil?

10. Which is the easiest component to test when a boiler is shut down because of a flame failure? How is this component tested?

Activity 7-1. Heating Systems

A steam heating system is used in a facility.

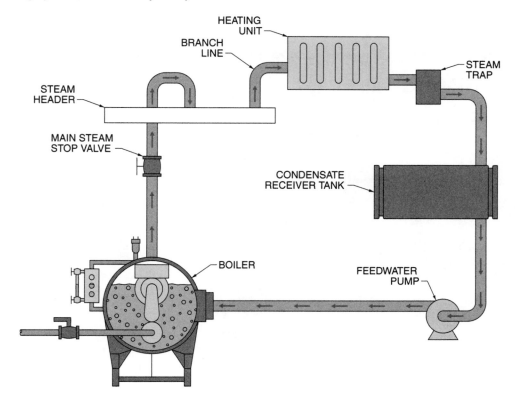

1. What changes occur to the water/steam as it moves through the system?

2. Indicate on the drawing where the latent heat is added to the water/steam by the system and where is it given up by the water/steam.

A hot water heating system is used in a facility.

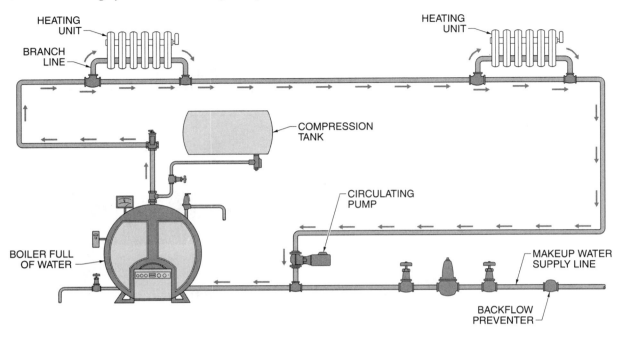

3. Does the water change state as it moves through the system?

4. Indicate on the drawing where the sensible heat is added to the water by the system and where it is given up by the water.

Activity 7-2. Low Water Fuel Cutoff

Water from a low water fuel cutoff is blown down and the burner is still firing.

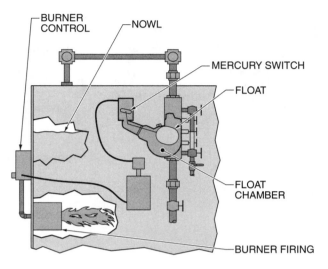

1. What is the problem in this situation?

2. How could this problem be repaired?

3. How could this problem be prevented from recurring?

4. What serious situation could result if this problem was not repaired?

Activity 7-3. Steam Traps

Temperature readings are taken at two points in the pipelines near a steam trap.

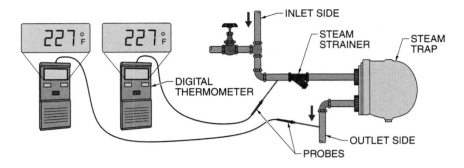

1. What is the problem in this situation?

2. What are two possible causes of this problem?

3. How could this problem be repaired?

4. How could this problem be prevented from recurring?

Activity 7-4. Natural Gas Line

A natural gas line feeds the fuel system of a boiler.

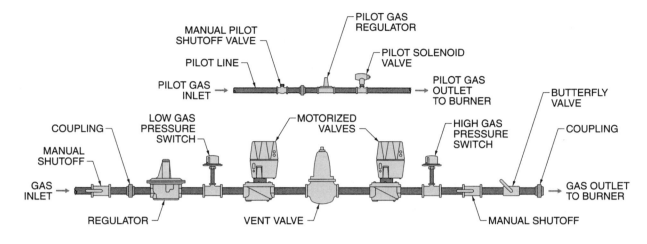

1. How is a low gas pressure cutoff tested?

2. What might happen to the boiler flame if the gas pressure is too low?

3. Why are there two motorized valves on the gas line?

4. What would happen if the solenoid valve on the pilot gas line was defective and would not open?

Activity 7-5. Flame Scanner Failure

The flame scanner from a boiler furnace is removed and tested by placing a hand over the sensor.

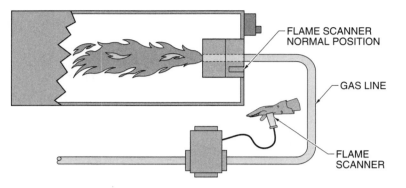

1. What is the problem in this situation?

2. How could this problem be repaired?

3. What serious situation could result if this problem was not repaired?

Activity 7-6. Water Column and Gauge Glass Blowdown

The gauge glass and water column of a boiler system are blown down. The water flows sluggishly into and out of the gauge glass and water column.

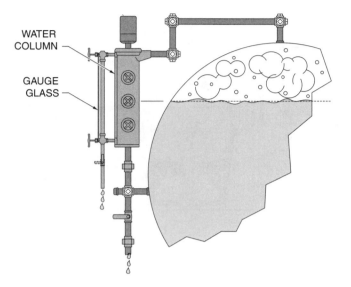

WATER
COLUMN

GAUGE
GLASS

1. What is the most likely cause of this problem?

2. How could this problem be repaired?

3. How could this problem be prevented from recurring?

4. How often should the water column and gauge glass be blown down?

Activity 7-7. Boiler Blowdown

A boiler is operating under normal conditions.

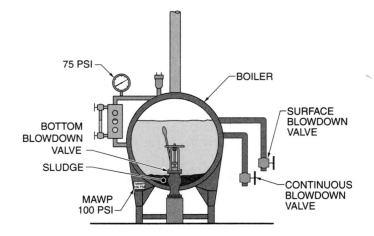

1. When should the boiler be blown down?

2. What determines how much water should be removed from the boiler?

3. Except when a boiler is being completely drained, what three conditions should be met before the boiler is blown down?

4. What could happen if these conditions are not met when this boiler is blown down?

5. When a boiler is emptied using the blowdown valves and has been washed out, what safety precaution should be taken with the blowdown valves?

6. Why are there two blowdown valves?

Activity 7-8. Low Water in the Boiler

A boiler has no water in the gauge glass. The steam pressure gauge reading is within the normal range and the boiler is still firing.

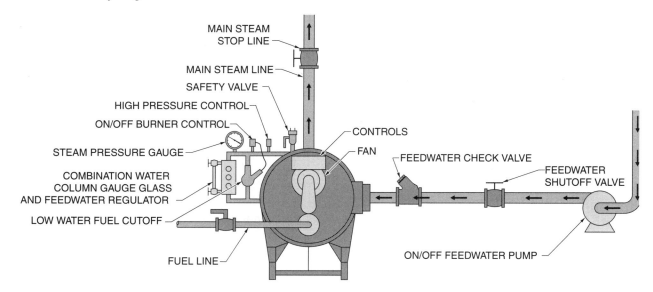

1. What should be done first?

2. What should be done next?

3. Which electrical devices might have failed and caused the problem?

4. What are possible causes of these failures?

5. Which system should be completely inspected to investigate these possible causes?

6. How could this problem be prevented from recurring?

Activity 7-9. High Water in the Boiler

A boiler has a gauge glass full of water. The steam pressure gauge reading is within the normal range and the boiler is still firing.

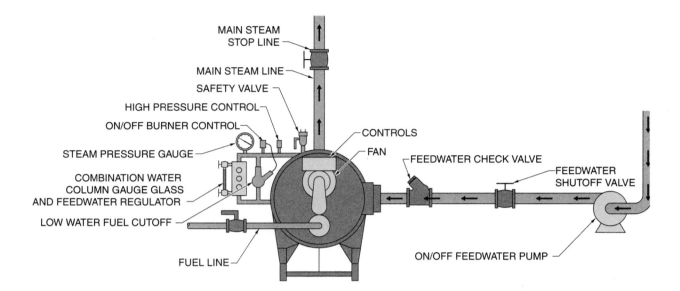

1. What should be done first?

2. What should be done next?

3. Which device might have failed and caused the problem?

4. What are possible causes of this failure?

5. Which system should be completely inspected to investigate these possible causes?

6. How could this problem be prevented from recurring?

Activity 7-10. Boiler Overpressure

A boiler steam pressure gauge reads 15 psi over the MAWP but the safety valve is not open and the boiler is still firing.

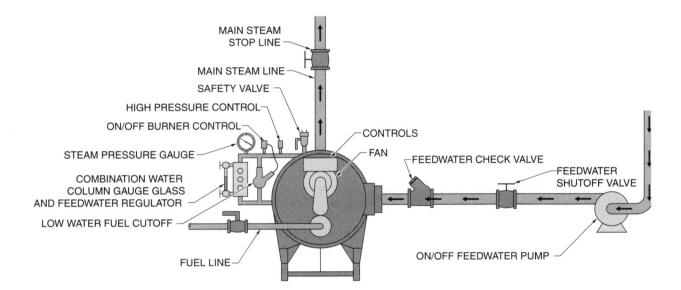

1. What should be done first? What should not be done?

2. What should be done next?

3. Which devices have failed and caused the problem?

4. What are possible causes of these failures?

5. How could this problem be corrected?

6. How could this problem be prevented from recurring?

Heating, Ventilating, and Air Conditioning Systems

Name _____ Date _____

Industrial Maintenance

_____ 1. A(n) ___ system is a system used to condition air by maintaining proper temperature, humidity, and air quality.

_____ 2. An air ___ is a device used to distribute conditioned air to spaces in a building.

_____ 3. Fan ___ is the volume of air a fan can move in a given period of time.

_____ 4. ___ air is the mixture of outside air and return air that is conditioned for use in a building.

T   F   5. HVAC air handler systems can be either constant volume or variable volume.

T   F   6. A closed-loop control system is a control system in which components are not affected by their own actions.

T   F   7. Air pressure does not vary inside a building.

_____ 8. A(n) ___ is a device that uses a liquid-filled tube to measure the difference in pressure between two locations.

_____ 9. A(n) ___ control system is a control system that uses compressed air to send variable signals from thermostats and controllers to controlled devices.

_____ 10. A pneumatic ___ is a device that uses air pressure to position HVAC components.
   A. thermostat   C. switch
   B. operator   D. none of the above

_____ 11. HVAC systems may contain ___.
   A. heating elements   C. air handlers
   B. refrigeration systems D. all of the above

_____ 12. ___ temperature is the temperature the HVAC system is set to maintain.

_____ 13. A(n) ___ is a movable plate that controls airflow.

_____ 14. A heating ___ is a finned heat exchanger that adds heat to the air.

_____ 15. A(n) ___ unit is a device that is located close to the zone and heats or cools air flowing through it.

T   F   16. An outside heat damper is completely closed when the signal causing it to operate is at its lowest level.

T   F   17. The two most common variables for determining fan size are capacity and static pressure.

T   F   18. Static pressure is the pressure exerted by airflow in a direction perpendicular to flow.

T   F   19. The "too hot/cold" call is the most common HVAC system complaint encountered.

_____ 20. An air ___ is a porous device that removes particles from air.

_____ 21. Indoor air ___ is a description of the type and quantity of contaminants in indoor air.

_____ 22. ___ humidity is the amount of moisture in the air compared to the amount of moisture the air would hold if it were saturated.

_____ 23. Poorly ___ HVAC systems and equipment can contribute to IAQ problems.
       A. designed   C. maintained
       B. installed   D. all of the above

_____ 24. ___ pressure is the pressure of airflow in the direction of flow.

_____ 25. A cooling ___ is a finned heat exchanger that removes heat from the air.

_____ 26. A(n) ___ box is a terminal unit that varies the amount of air flowing into a zone.

T   F 27. Most HVAC systems are open-loop systems.

T   F 28. The efficiency of a filter is rated by the size of particles it can trap.

_____ 29. ___ cycling is the increase in the frequency of system operation due to improper feedback.
       A. Temporary   C. Sporadic
       B. Intermittent   D. Short

_____ 30. ___ is the condition that occurs when people cannot sense a difference between themselves and the surrounding air.

Pneumatic Operators

_____ 1. Piston

_____ 2. Diaphragm

_____ 3. Bellows

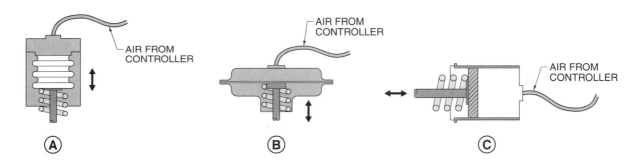

Fan Capacity

_____ 1. A 22″, 2 HP fan operating at 390 rpm and ¼″ WC moves ___ cfm of air.

_____ 2. If the motor on the fan in No. 1 was increased to 3 HP, the fan would move ___ cfm of air.

_____ 3. If the static pressure on the fan in No. 2 was increased to ½″ WC, the fan would move ___ cfm of air.

	FAN CAPACITY*							
Wheel Dia†	Static Pressure‡						RPM	HP
	⅛	¼	½	¾	1	1¼		
22	7600	7000	5450	3500	—	—	390	2
	8700	8300	7150	5400	—	—	445	3
	10,500	10,100	9500	8350	7100	4800	530	5
	12,000	11,450	10,900	10,200	9500	8100	600	7½

* in cfm
† in in.
‡ in in. WC

Direct Digital Control Systems

_____ 1. Main computer

_____ 2. Auxiliary computer

_____ 3. Portable computer

_____ 4. Controller

_____ 5. Sensor

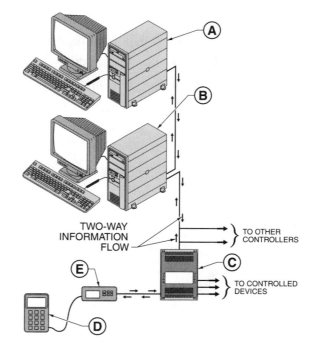

Variable Air Volume (VAV) Box

_____ 1. Controller

_____ 2. Supply air

_____ 3. Heating element

_____ 4. Damper

_____ 5. Damper motor

_____ 6. Diffuser

_____ 7. Temperature measured by thermostat

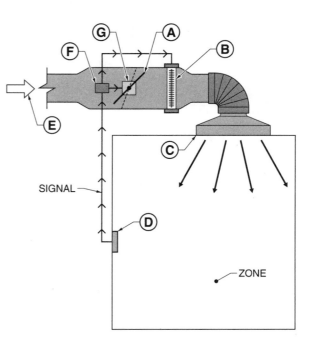

Fans

_____ **1.** Radial flow, direct drive

_____ **2.** Radial flow, indirect drive

_____ **3.** Axial flow, direct drive

_____ **4.** Axial flow, indirect drive

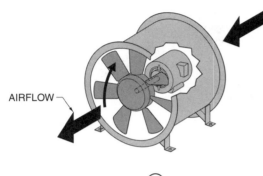

AIRFLOW

Ⓐ

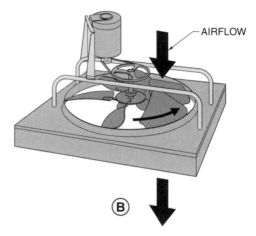

AIRFLOW

Ⓑ

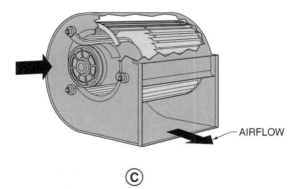

AIRFLOW

Ⓒ

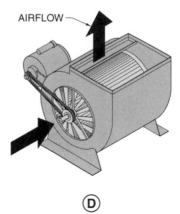

AIRFLOW

Ⓓ

Heating, Ventilating, and Air Conditioning Systems

8

Name _____   Date _____

Short Answer Questions

1. What does it mean when air is described as conditioned?

2. Define setpoint.

3. How is a closed-loop system different from an open-loop system?

4. What does increasing efficiency mean in terms of the particle size a filter will trap?

5. What happens when the plates of an electrostatic precipitator become dirty?

6. List the important qualities of compressed air to be used in HVAC control systems.

7. Describe two ways a DDC system can save energy.

8. What maintenance does a DDC system require?

9. Describe a basic procedure for dealing with a "too hot/cold" call.

10. Why should the hands and body be kept away from a thermometer when taking a temperature reading at the thermostat?

11. What will happen to a sensor signal that is sent along a signal wire that is too long or has a loose connection point? (Think about Ohm's law.)

12. Why must a room and its contents be dried completely or replaced if the room has been flooded?

13. Why is an effective preventive maintenance program for an HVAC system the key to preventing indoor air quality problems?

Activity 8-1. Air Handler Operation

The air handler must be adjusted to cool the building space when it is hot outside.

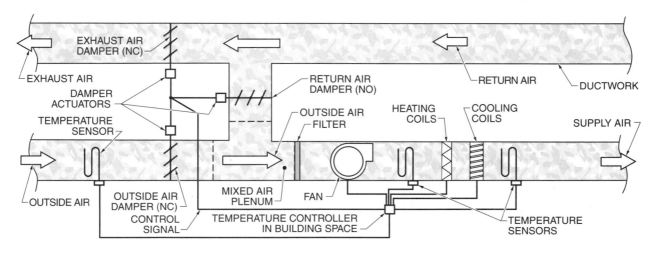

1. How should the outside, exhaust, and return air dampers be positioned?

2. Which of the coils will be operating?

The air handler must be adjusted to cool the building space when it is cool outside.

3. How should the outside, exhaust, and return air dampers be positioned?

4. Which of the coils will be operating?

The air handler must be adjusted to heat the building space when it is cold outside.

5. How should the outside, exhaust, and return air dampers be positioned?

6. Which of the coils will be operating?

7. What problem would occur if the outside air damper was locked in the closed position?

8. What problem would occur if the return air damper was stuck closed?

9. What maintenance would this unit require?

Activity 8-2. Variable Air Volume Box

A variable air volume box is used in a system to control the temperature of a zone.

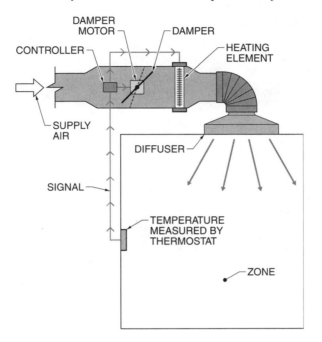

1. Why is this VAV box considered a closed-loop system?

2. What might occur if the thermostat was damaged and did not send a signal to the controller?

3. Which position should the damper be at when heating is required?

4. Which position should the damper be at when cooling is required?

The zone includes a bookcase that is placed in front of the thermostat.

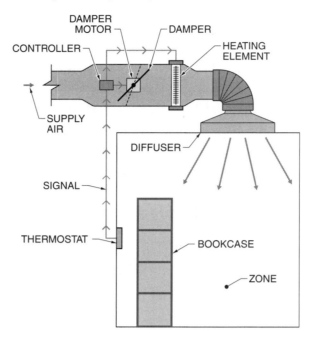

5. What is the problem in this situation?

The zone includes an office partition that divides the room.

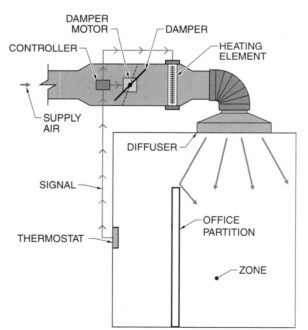

6. What is the problem in this situation?

Activity 8-3. Building Pressures

Chemicals are stored in a closet with a fan that exhausts chemical fumes outside.

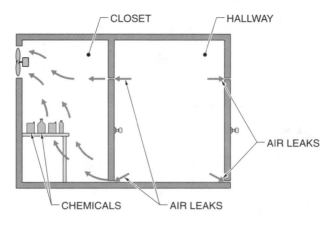

1. What is the air pressure in the closet relative to the air pressure in the hallway?

2. What would happen to the air pressure in the closet if the exhaust fan failed?

3. What problem might develop in the hallway if the exhaust fan failed?

4. What basic maintenance would a belt-driven exhaust fan require?

5. Should the exhaust air from this chemical closet be added to the overall return air for an air handler?

6. What problem might be caused if air leaked from outside into the hallway?

7. Where should air from a chemical closet or similar area be vented?

Activity 8-4. Filters

A diaphragm gauge is attached to an air handler system to show the pressure drop across a filter.

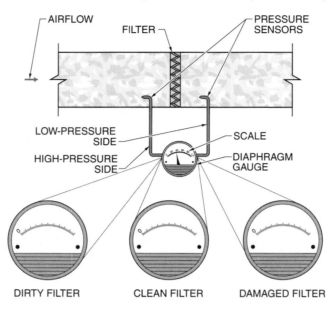

1. Sketch the approximate needle position on the gauge if the filter is very dirty and plugged with dirt particles.

2. Sketch the approximate needle position on the gauge if the filter is clean.

3. Sketch the approximate needle position if the filter is damaged and air is blowing around the filter.

4. What might happen to airflow if the air filters were changed from low-efficiency to high-efficiency filters?

5. What might happen to the supply air fan?

6. Why might a filter be changed long before it becomes clogged?

Activity 8-5. Valve Signals

A normally open valve operator has an open to closed signal range of 4 psi to 8 psi.

1. What position will the valve be at when the air pressure signal is 2 psi?

2. What position will the valve be at when the air pressure signal is 4 psi?

3. What position will the valve be at when the air pressure signal is 6 psi?

4. What position will the valve be at when the air pressure signal is 8 psi?

5. What position will the valve be at when the air pressure signal is 10 psi?

Activity 8-6. Three-Way Valve

A three-way valve controls water flow through or around a cooling coil. The valve is currently actuated to provide maximum cooling.

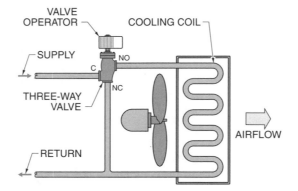

1. Indicate the direction of chilled water flow with arrows.

The three-way valve is set to provide no cooling.

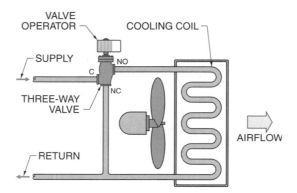

2. Indicate the direction of chilled water flow with arrows.

3. If the control signal was removed from the three-way valve, where would the water flow?

4. If the fan failed, how would water flow be affected?

Name _____   Date _____

Industrial Maintenance

_____ **1.** A(n) ___ is a substance that separates moving (bearing) surfaces to reduce the friction and/or wear between them.

_____ **2.** ___ is the combination of metal and oxygen into metal oxides.

_____ **3.** A(n) ___ is a machine component used to reduce friction and maintain clearance between stationary and moving parts.

T   F   **4.** A radial load is a load applied parallel to the rotating shaft.

T   F   **5.** A cage is an antifriction bearing component used to maintain the position and alignment of the rolling elements.

T   F   **6.** Any two gears that mesh rotate in opposite directions.

_____ **7.** The gear diameter determines the ___ of teeth on a gear.
  A. number   C. size
  B. type   D. none of the above

_____ **8.** A cam ___ is a machine part that contacts the cam and moves in a designated path.
  A. ear   C. tracer
  B. lobe   D. follower

_____ **9.** A(n) ___ is a device used to connect a mechanical drive to a prime mover.

_____ **10.** A(n) ___ is a device used to remove gears, pulleys, sprockets, bearings, and couplings from a shaft or housing.

T   F   **11.** Abrasive wear is wear that occurs when a hard surface rubs against a softer surface.

T   F   **12.** The grease dropping point is the temperature at which the thickening agent of a grease turns to a liquid.

_____ **13.** A(n) ___ is a flexible loop that connects two or more pulleys for transferring rotational power.

_____ **14.** Common lubricating grease is not suitable for operating temperatures above ___°F.

_____ **15.** A(n) ___ cup is a pressurized grease reservoir that provides constant lubrication to a bearing.

_____ **16.** An oil ___ is a device used to contain oil inside a housing.

_____ **17.** Belt ___ is the natural movement of the belt on the face of the pulley when it is subjected to changes in tension.

_____ **18.** Proper belt tension should result in approximately ___″ of belt deflection for every inch of span between pulley centers.

_____ **19.** A(n) ___ is a sealed container that has an input shaft and an output shaft and houses at least one set of mating gears.

T   F   **20.** Always ensure that power is turned OFF, locked out, and tagged out before performing any preventive maintenance procedures.

_____ **21.** ___ are microscopic peaks and valleys left over from the machining process.

_____ 22. ___ is the measure of the resistance of a fluid's molecules to move past each other.

_____ 23. ___ friction is friction that occurs when one surface moves across another or both surfaces move in opposite directions.

T   F 24. Lubricants reduce the operating temperatures of machine parts by transferring heat from the metal surfaces to the lubricant.

T   F 25. An axial load is a load applied perpendicular to the rotating shaft.

_____ 26. A(n) ___ metal is a metal that does not contain iron.

_____ 27. A(n) ___ bearing is a bearing designed to provide low-friction movement of a mechanical device that moves in a straight line.

_____ 28. A(n) ___ is a machine part that transmits motion using an irregular external or internal surface.

_____ 29. Pullers are sized by ___.
    A. pressure   C. reach
    B. spread   D. all of the above

_____ 30. A(n) ___ bearing is a bearing that contains moving elements, which provide a low-friction support surface for rotating on sliding surfaces.
    A. friction   C. wear
    B. antifriction   D. antiwear

_____ 31. A belt drive is a(n) ___ drive system that uses a belt and pulleys to transfer power between two surfaces.
    A. electronic   C. mechanical
    B. pneumatic   D. all of the above

_____ 32. A(n) ___ is a series of interconnected links that form a loop.

_____ 33. A(n) ___ coupling is a device that joins two shafts that are precisely aligned within a common frame.
    A. rigid   C. chain
    B. flexible   D. elastomeric

T   F 34. Pullers may be mechanically or hydraulically operated.

T   F 35. Thermography is a predictive maintenance procedure that uses heat energy emitted from non-operating equipment to analyze the status of moving components.

T   F 36. Heating a bearing increases the size of the bearing, allowing it to slip over a shaft.

_____ 37. ___ is the flaking off of a metal surface.

_____ 38. ___-belts are the most frequently used for belt drive systems.

_____ 39. A(n) ___ sprocket is a sprocket that has no hub.

_____ 40. ___ is the distance between corresponding points on an adjacent pair of evenly spaced projections.

Belt Tension

_____ 1. Drive pulley

_____ 2. Driven pulley

_____ 3. Tight side

_____ 4. Slack side

Installing Belts

List steps in sequential order.

_____	**1.** Check pulley alignment
_____	**2.** Check belt tension
_____	**3.** Select proper belt
_____	**4.** Move motor back using pry bar
_____	**5.** Replace guard and remove lockout/tagout
_____	**6.** Move pulleys to required center-to-center distance and slide belt over pulleys

A. Step 1
B. Step 2
C. Step 3
D. Step 4
E. Step 5
F. Step 6

Roller Bearings

_____	**1.** Needle
_____	**2.** Cylindrical
_____	**3.** Spherical
_____	**4.** Tapered

Belts

_____	**1.** Single V-belt
_____	**2.** Multiple V-belt
_____	**3.** Link-type V-belt
_____	**4.** Double-sided timing belt
_____	**5.** Flat belt

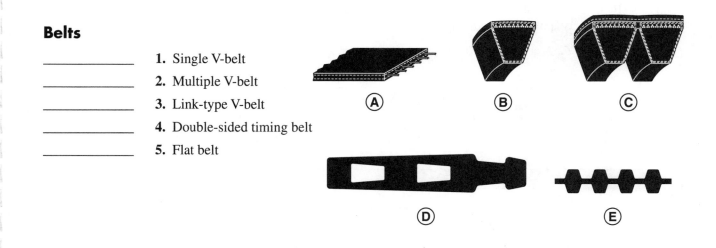

Removing Belts

List steps in sequential order.

_____ **1.** Remove belt guard

_____ **2.** Turn OFF, lock out, and tag out machine

_____ **3.** Loosen belt tension

_____ **4.** Remove old belt and check pulley tension

A. Step 1

B. Step 2

C. Step 3

D. Step 4

Roller Chain

_____ **1.** Pin

_____ **2.** Pitch

_____ **3.** Roller

_____ **4.** Roller width

_____ **5.** Roller diameter

_____ **6.** Code

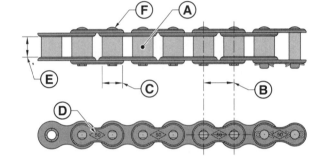

Belt Materials

_____ **1.** Natural rubber belt material has ___ oil resistance.

_____ **2.** Neoprene belt material has ___ tear resistance.

T   F   **3.** Natural rubber, neoprene, and polyurethane belt materials have excellent abrasion resistance.

T   F   **4.** Natural rubber belts operate in the same temperature range as polyurethane belts.

_____ **5.** A neoprene belt has ___ solvent resistance.

BELT MATERIALS							
Material	Tensile Range*	Temperature Range†	Solvent Resistant	Oil Resistant	Abrasion Resistant	Tear Resistant	Aging Weather
Natural Rubber	500 – 3500	−60 to 175	Poor	Poor	Excellent	Excellent	Poor
Neoprene	500 – 3000	−50 to 185	Fair	Fair	Excellent	Good	Good
Polyurethane	500 – 600	−30 to 175	Poor	Good	Excellent	Excellent	Excellent

* in psi
† in °F

Gears

_____   **1.** Helical

_____   **2.** Bevel

_____   **3.** Worm

_____   **4.** Miter

_____   **5.** Herringbone

_____   **6.** Spur, external

_____   **7.** Spur, internal

_____   **8.** Spur, rack and pinion

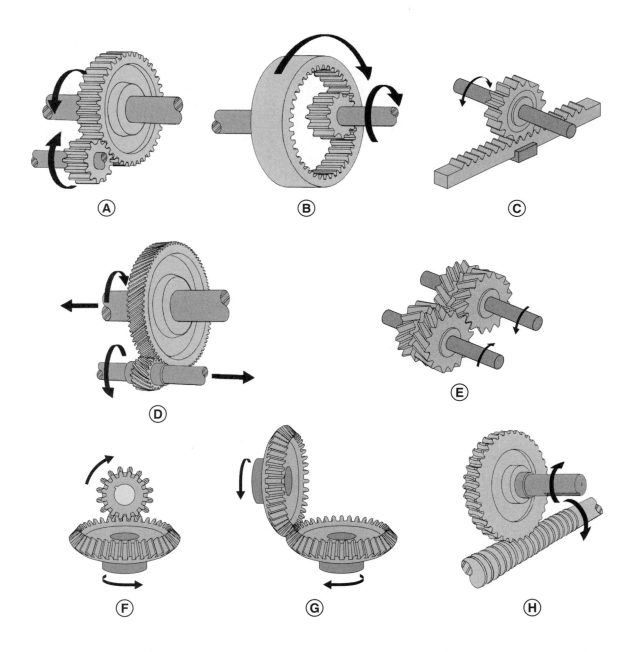

Gear Rotation

_____ **1.** Gear B turns in a(n) ___ rotation.

_____ **2.** Gear C turns in a(n) ___ rotation.

  T   F   **3.** Gear C and D turn at the same speed.

  T   F   **4.** Gear B turns slower than Gear A.

_____ **5.** Gear D turns in a(n) ___ rotation.

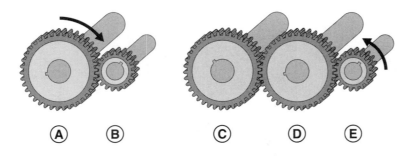

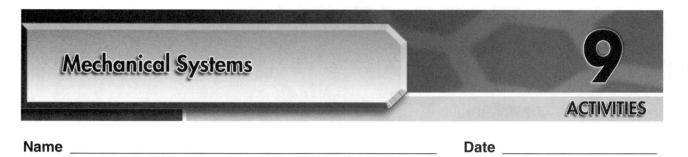

Name _____ **Date** _____

Activity 9-1. Lubrication

Oil from a gearbox with abrasive wear damage is analyzed.

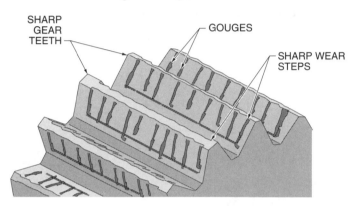

SHARP GEAR TEETH

GOUGES

SHARP WEAR STEPS

1. What type of contaminants would be found?

Corrosion is produced by water in the oil. The water causes rust and creates acid that removes metal from gear teeth.

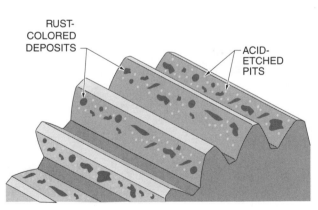

RUST-COLORED DEPOSITS

ACID-ETCHED PITS

2. Which part of an oil analysis report would indicate that a gearbox had this type of contamination?

175

A new gearbox is installed, lubricated, and started up for the first time.

3. Where do asperities go after the break-in period?

4. What damage would occur if the microscopic layer of lubrication was disrupted and metal-to-metal contact occurred?

5. Why might it be better to have just a few types of general-duty lubricants than a large number of specific application greases?

6. Why should caps be kept on grease fittings?

Activity 9-2. Bearings

A bearing is installed by using a pressing tool to apply force evenly around the bearing.

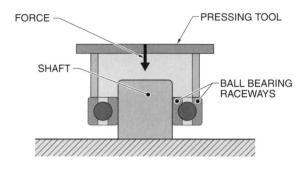

1. What problem will develop from this situation?

A bearing is installed correctly, but continues to receive force from the pressing tool after it is seated in the housing.

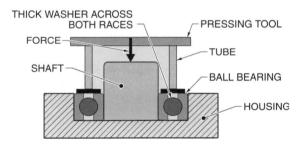

2. What problem will develop from this situation?

3. Why does overlubrication damage a bearing?

4. Why does most bearing wear occur at equipment startup?

5. Why is it important to try to remove a bearing without damaging it?

Activity 9-3. Mechanical Drive Systems

Answer the following questions about mechanical drive systems.

1. Why should sprockets be inspected when removing or inspecting a chain?

2. Why must all belts in a multiple belt drive be changed when one belt is changed?

3. What is the purpose of analyzing the cause of a bearing, gear, or chain or belt drive failure?

4. How might the operation of a cam and cam follower be affected by misalignment?

5. Why are many variable-speed belt drives being replaced by electronic speed controls?

Activity 9-4. Belt Tensioning

Calculate the appropriate belt deflection for proper tension based on the following belt drive arrangements. There should be ¹⁄₆₄″(0.0156″) of deflection from a straightedge for each inch of span length.

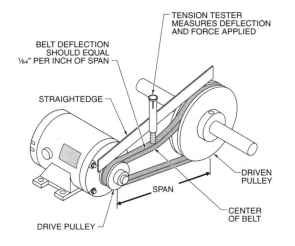

$h = L \times \frac{1}{64}''$

where
h = deflection (in in.)
L = center-to-center span length between the pulleys (in in.)

1. The center-to-center distance of a belt drive is 12″.

2. The center-to-center distance of a belt drive is 48″.

3. The center-to-center distance of a belt drive is 21″.

4. The center-to-center distance of a belt drive is 33.5″.

5. Why must belt tension be checked again one or two days after installing new belts?

Activity 9-5. Alignment

A new motor is installed to operate a pump and must be checked for proper alignment.

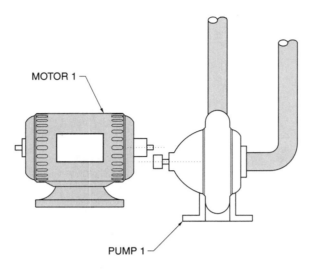

MOTOR 1

PUMP 1

1. Indicate with an arrow or arrows how the motor must be moved to correct the alignment problem.

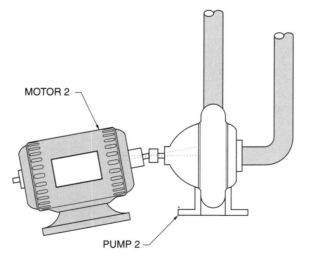

MOTOR 2

PUMP 2

2. Indicate with an arrow or arrows how the motor must be moved to correct the alignment problem.

3. Which is the most accurate method of alignment: string and straightedge, dial indicator, or laser alignment?

4. For a small pump with a flexible coupling, which alignment method would be appropriate?

5. For a high-speed turbine generator, which alignment method would be appropriate?

6. Will shaft misalignment add to the current draw of the motor driving the load?

7. What might an oil stain near the shaft coming out of a gearbox indicate?

8. Why might string be used to help align belt pulleys instead of a straightedge?

Name _____ Date _____

Industrial Maintenance

_____ **1.** A(n) ___ is a noncompressible fluid that can readily flow and assume the shape of an enclosed space.

_____ **2.** ___ is the number of unit squares equal to the surface of an object.

T   F   **3.** If area is constant, force increases as pressure increases.

_____ **4.** A(n) ___ is a container for storing fluid under little or no pressure.

_____ **5.** ___ is the volume of a hydraulic oil moved during each revolution, stroke, or cycle of a pump.

T   F   **6.** An axial reciprocating pump is a pump that consists of pistons located perpendicular to the pump shaft.

T   F   **7.** Hydraulic hose is less susceptible to damage from vibration or movement than rigid pipe.

_____ **8.** A(n) ___ is a device that controls the pressure, direction, or rate of fluid flow.

_____ **9.** ___ is allowing a pump to run against little or no pressure.
     A. Down-sizing   C. Depressurizing
     B. Unloading   D. none of the above

_____ **10.** A(n) ___ is a container in which fluid is stored under pressure.
     A. basin   C. well
     B. accumulator   D. none of the above

_____ **11.** A(n) ___ system is a fluid power system that transmits energy using a gas (typically compressed air).

_____ **12.** An air ___ is a component that takes air from the atmosphere and compresses it to increase its pressure.

T   F   **13.** The warmer the air drawn into a compressor, the more efficiently the compressor operates.

T   F   **14.** Pneumatic tools present no danger of electrical shock.

_____ **15.** An oil and moisture ___ is a device that removes oil and water droplets from a system by forcing compressed air to change direction quickly.

_____ **16.** A(n) ___ is a component that injects a mist of oil into the compressed air line for lubrication of pneumatic tools and internal motor parts.

_____ **17.** A(n) ___ valve is a valve that allows the pressure against the discharge valves to be released at startup.

T   F   **18.** The smaller the micron number of filter material, the poorer the filtering capability.

T   F   **19.** Hydraulic motor speed is controlled by the rate of oil flow.

_____ **20.** Single-acting cylinders have a piston in the cylinder that is extended by applied hydraulic oil pressure and retracted by ___.
     A. the weight of the load   C. spring
     B. gravity   D. all of the above

_____ 21. A(n) ___ system is a fluid power system that transmits energy in an enclosed space using a liquid under pressure.

_____ 22. ___ is anything that changes or tends to change the state of rest or motion of a body.

_____ 23. ___ is the force per unit area.

_____ 24. A(n) ___ is a component that produces motion from some other form of energy.

_____ 25. A(n) ___ control valve is a valve that regulates the volume of hydraulic oil flowing to components in a system.

T   F   26. All hydraulic systems consist of a source, pathway(s), and load(s).

_____ 27. A(n) ___ is a mechanical device that causes fluid to flow.

_____ 28. A(n) ___ is a flexible tube used for carrying fluids under pressure.

_____ 29. A(n) ___ valve is a valve in which the valve seating element pops open to allow flow in one direction.

_____ 30. A(n) ___ is a component that converts fluid pressure into linear mechanical force.

_____ 31. A(n) ___ motor is a device that converts hydraulic energy into rotation.

T   F   32. Hoses should be stored in cool, dry areas away from direct sunlight.

T   F   33. Never kink or fold back a hose to stop flow.

_____ 34. ___ is the process in which microscopic gas bubbles expand in a vacuum and suddenly implode when entering a pressurized area.

_____ 35. A(n) ___ is a device that allows the compressor to operate without adding pressure to the receiver.

_____ 36. A(n) ___ is an air tank that stores compressed air and allows it to cool before use.

T   F   37. Copper, aluminum, or plastic pipe is used only in low-pressure hydraulic applications.

T   F   38. Pneumatic systems usually operate at lower pressures than hydraulic systems.

_____ 39. A(n) ___ cylinder is a cylinder that slows piston movement to provide a gradual stop.

_____ 40. A(n) ___ compressor is compressor that uses pistons moving back and forth to increase fluid pressure.

Vane Pumps

_____ 1. Housing

_____ 2. Shaft

_____ 3. Rotor

_____ 4. Inlet

_____ 5. Outlet

_____ 6. Seal

_____ 7. Movable vanes

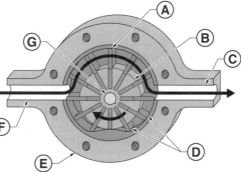

Gear Pumps

_____ **1.** Gerotor

_____ **2.** External

_____ **3.** Internal

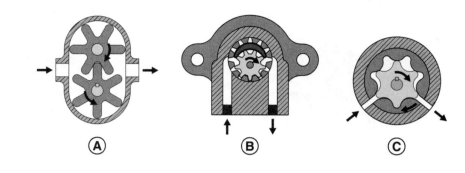

Pneumatic Systems

_____ **1.** Air receiver

_____ **2.** Shutoff valve

_____ **3.** Lubricator

_____ **4.** Regulator

_____ **5.** Filter

_____ **6.** Pressure-relief valve

_____ **7.** Compressor

_____ **8.** Inlet air cleaner

_____ **9.** Electrical control panel

_____ **10.** Automatic drains

_____ **11.** Refrigerant dryer

_____ **12.** Aftercooler

_____ **13.** Pressure gauge

_____ **14.** Oil and moisture separator

_____ **15.** Intercooler

_____ **16.** Main line

_____ **17.** High pressure cutout and compressor operating controls

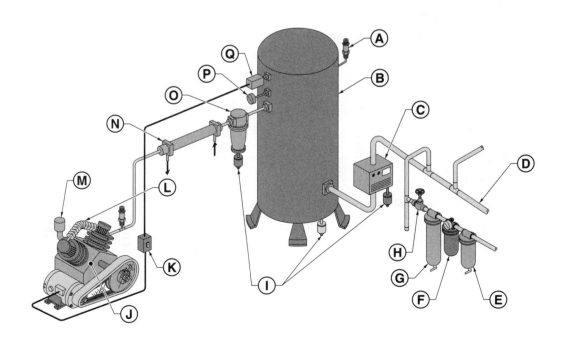

Hydraulic Hose Coupling

_____ **1.** Seal

_____ **2.** Spring

_____ **3.** Sleeve

_____ **4.** Poppet valve

_____ **5.** Poppet seal

_____ **6.** Valve stop

_____ **7.** Coupling threads

_____ **8.** Ball locking mechanism

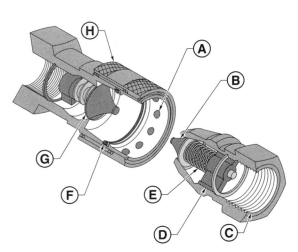

Hydraulic Force

_____ **1.** A pressure of ___ psi is required at A.

_____ **2.** The area of the piston required at B is ___ sq in.

_____ **3.** A force of ___ lb is produced at C.

_____ **4.** A force of ___ lb is produced at D.

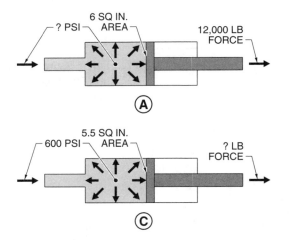

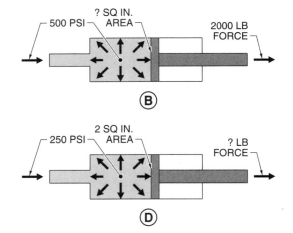

Tool Stations

_____ **1.** Air-powered tool

_____ **2.** Quick disconnect

_____ **3.** Regulator

_____ **4.** Filter

_____ **5.** Shutoff valve

_____ **6.** Lubricator

_____ **7.** Flexible air line

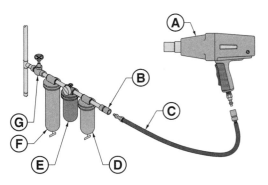

Hydraulic System Components — Pictorial

_____   **1.** Reservoir

_____   **2.** Filter

_____   **3.** Pump

_____   **4.** Return line

_____   **5.** Directional control valve

_____   **6.** Pressure-relief valve

_____   **7.** Pressure gauge

_____   **8.** Piston rod

_____   **9.** Piston

_____   **10.** Cylinder

_____   **11.** Flow control valve

_____   **12.** Check valve

_____   **13.** Electric motor

_____   **14.** Rod end

_____   **15.** Cap end

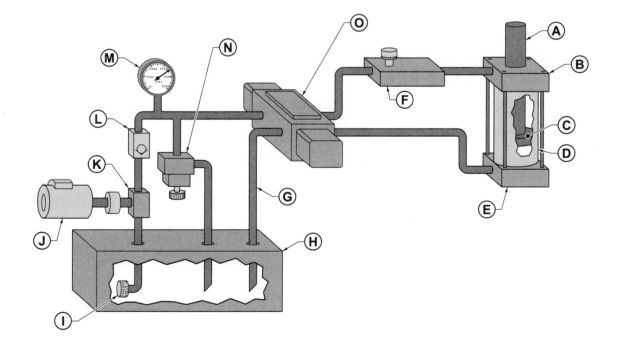

Hydraulic System Components — Schematic

_____   **1.** Piston rod

_____   **2.** Cap end

_____   **3.** Rod end

_____   **4.** Flow control valve

_____   **5.** Directional control valve

_____   **6.** Pressure-relief valve

_____   **7.** Check valve

_____   **8.** Cylinder

_____   **9.** Reservoir

_____   **10.** Filter

_____   **11.** Pump

_____   **12.** Pressure gauge

_____   **13.** Return line

_____   **14.** Electric motor

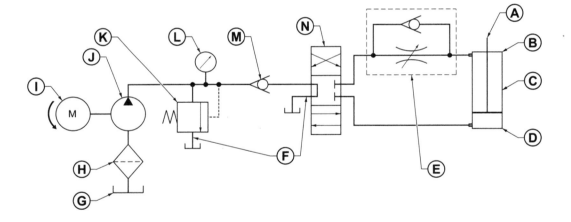

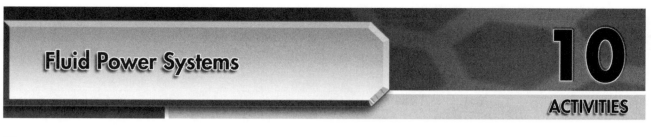

Name _____   **Date** _____

Activity 10-1. Pump Operation

An external gear pump is used to circulate oil through a hydraulic system.

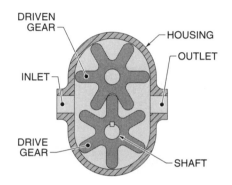

1. Label the high- and low-pressure areas.

2. Sketch in the direction of oil flow into, out of, and through the pump.

3. Indicate and label two places where the rotor seals with the pump housing.

4. What problem will occur if oil flow is restricted at the pump inlet?

189

5. What would the outlet oil look like if there were a leak on the inlet side of the pump?

6. How would a leak in the inlet side of the pump be located?

7. What problem might occur if the oil is extremely cold?

8. Does a pump develop flow or pressure?

Activity 10-2. Pressure and Flow Control Valves

A pressure relief valve is a valve that sets a maximum operating pressure level for a circuit to protect the circuit from overpressure.

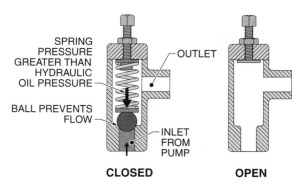

1. Sketch in the position of the ball and spring and the direction of oil flow in the pressure-relief valve when it is open.

A pressure-reducing valve is a valve that limits the maximum pressure at its outlet, regardless of the inlet pressure.

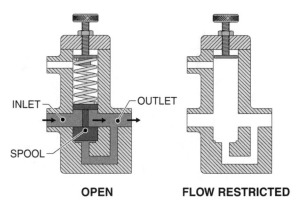

2. Sketch in the position of the spool and spring and the direction of oil flow in the pressure-reducing valve when it is restricting flow.

A pressure-sequence valve is a pressure-operated valve that diverts flow to a secondary actuator while holding pressure on the primary actuator at a predetermined minimum value after the primary actuator completes its travel.

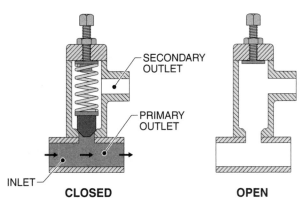

CLOSED   **OPEN**

3. Sketch in the position of the spool and spring and the direction of oil flow in the pressure-sequencing valve when it is directing oil to the secondary outlet.

An unloading valve is a pressure control valve that directs hydraulic oil from the pump to the reservoir after system pressure has been reached.

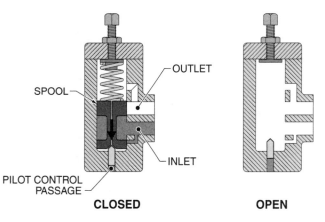

CLOSED   **OPEN**

4. Sketch in the position of the spool and spring and the direction of oil flow in the unloading valve when it is open.

5. Why should the spring tension not be adjusted when no pressure or flow measurement equipment is attached to the system?

6. Why must system specifications be consulted when adjusting pressure or flow?

7. What two dangerous situations could occur if pressure and flow are altered carelessly?

8. In which two places must changes to pressure and flow be noted?

9. What part of an unloading valve is most affected by dirty oil?

10. What long-term problem could develop if the hydraulic oil was not sealing the metal parts of these valves properly?

Activity 10-3. Unloading Valves

A hydraulic system includes an unloading valve to direct oil back to the reservoir when a specific pressure has been reached. The unloading valve is currently closed.

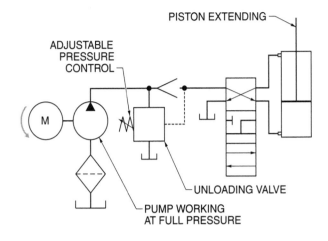

1. Sketch in the check valve position, the unloading valve position, and oil flow directions.

System pressure reaches a certain level and the unloading valve opens.

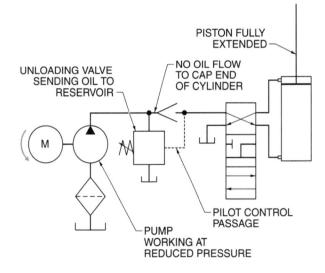

2. Sketch in the check valve position, the unloading valve position, and oil flow directions.

3. What is a likely cause of a system with an unloading valve not supplying enough pressure to the loads?

4. What is a likely cause of a system with an unloading valve not unloading?

5. What damage could occur if the unloading valve did not unload at its set pressure?

Activity 10-4. Directional Control Valves

A directional control valve is used in a hydraulic piston control circuit.

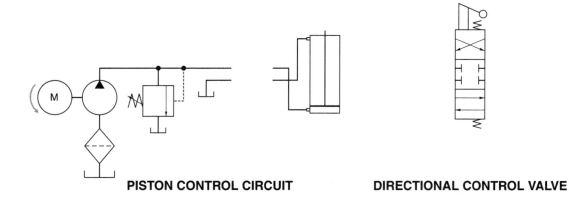

PISTON CONTROL CIRCUIT   **DIRECTIONAL CONTROL VALVE**

1. Sketch the directional control valve in the correct position to extend the piston rod.

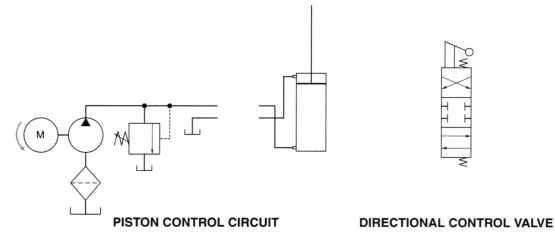

PISTON CONTROL CIRCUIT   **DIRECTIONAL CONTROL VALVE**

2. Sketch the directional control valve in the correct position to retract the piston rod.

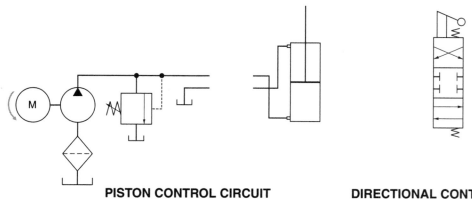

PISTON CONTROL CIRCUIT   **DIRECTIONAL CONTROL VALVE**

3. Sketch the directional control valve in the neutral position.

4. List two problems that could cause the piston to slowly retract in the neutral position.

5. Is the piston single or double acting?

6. Is the piston balanced or unbalanced?

7. If the piston becomes damaged by slamming hard as it retracted and extended, what type of cylinder could be substituted to prevent this damage?

8. What maintenance does this hydraulic system require?

Activity 10-5. Pneumatic Systems

Answer the following questions about pneumatic systems and their components.

1. What is the purpose of the intercooler?

2. Is the operation of the high-pressure cutout and the operating control similar to controls on a boiler system?

3. Why must oil and water be removed from the compressed air?

4. How does a refrigerated dryer remove moisture from the air?

5. What dangerous situation can occur if a pressurized air hose breaks, and how should this situation be handled?

6. Why are pneumatic systems fitted with pressure relief valves?

7. Should an oil lubricator be installed in an air system supplying HVAC controls or medical tools?

8. Should a filter and pressure regulator be installed in an air system supplying HVAC controls or medical tools?

9. What might happen to the temperature of the compressed air if it was being used so quickly that it flowed directly through the receiver rather than being held there for several hours before use?

Name _____ Date _____

Industrial Maintenance

T   F   **1.** Safety is the most important concern when performing maintenance and troubleshooting work.

T   F   **2.** New equipment manufacturers do not specify the maintenance requirements that must be completed to maintain the warranty.

T   F   **3.** A reliable measure of a PM program is the rate of breakdowns that require troubleshooting.

_____   **4.** ___ maintenance is scheduled work required to keep equipment in peak operating condition.

_____   **5.** ___ is the systematic elimination of the cause of system problems in order to determine the best solutions.

T   F   **6.** Maintenance personnel do not operate equipment as part of their duties.

T   F   **7.** Logbook entries may be made hourly, several times each day, or weekly, depending on the size of the equipment and the amount of automatic monitoring equipment used.

T   F   **8.** Troubleshooters must consider the entire system when trying to identify and repair a problem.

T   F   **9.** Closed-loop control systems are less common than open-loop control systems.

T   F   **10.** Troubleshooting can be more complicated if time or distance separates the reaction to changes made in a system.

T   F   **11.** Most manufacturers supply troubleshooting recommendations and system diagnostic guides with equipment.

T   F   **12.** Troubleshooting information may be presented as a flow chart.

_____   **13.** A troubleshooting ___ is a record of a specific problem that occurs in a particular piece of equipment.

_____   **14.** Boilers supply ___ or hot water for use in heating or in production processes.

_____   **15.** Systems ___ is the consideration of an entire system when working on any part of the system.

T   F   **16.** Performing excessive preventive maintenance work drives up the cost of maintenance operations.

T   F   **17.** Most mechanical, electrical, and electronic systems are closed-loop systems.

T   F   **18.** Operator's manuals may contain troubleshooting information printed in chart form.

T   F   **19.** Intermittent problems are easier to diagnose than constant problems.

T   F   **20.** Troubleshooting and maintenance advice in operator's manuals is the most commonly used resource in troubleshooting problems.

T   F   **21.** A troubleshooting report is not required if a problem has been solved.

T   F   **22.** Over time, most equipment develops tendencies or problems that repeat.

T   F   **23.** Troubleshooting reports that are incorporated into a plant preventive maintenance system become part of the equipment history for each machine.

T   F   **24.** R-22 refrigerant is being phased out.

_____   **25.** A(n) ___-loop control system is a control system in which the result of an output is fed back into the controller as an input.

Control Systems

_____   **1.** The system at ___ is an open-loop control system.

_____   **2.** The system at ___ is a closed-loop control system.

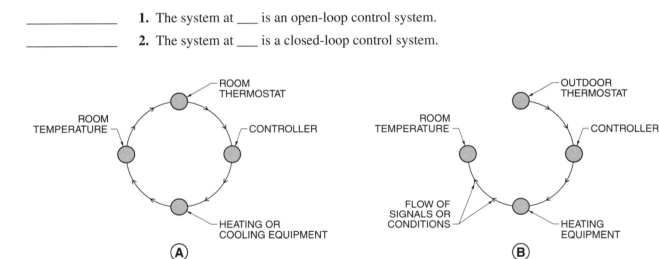

Flow Chart Symbols

_____   **1.** The symbol at ___ indicates direction.

_____   **2.** The symbol at ___ indicates the beginning or end.

_____   **3.** The symbol at ___ contains questions.

_____   **4.** The symbol at ___ contains a set of instructions.

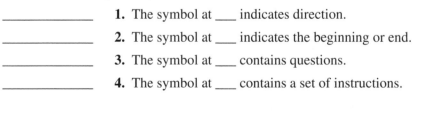

Troubleshooting Report

_____ **1.** The equipment identification number of the piece of equipment on this report is ___.

T　　F　　**2.** Old and new chain was found on the broken chain.

T　　F　　**3.** The chain was replaced.

_____ **4.** The problem occurred on Product Line # ___.

_____ **5.** The overload trip mechanism was not operating due to ___ damage.

T　　F　　**6.** The conveyor continued to run throughout the problem.

_____ **7.** The ___, overloads, and magnetic motor starter were replaced.

_____ **8.** The symptom(s) indicating a problem was/were ___.
　　A. a loud snap and grinding sound　　C. the conveyor stopping suddenly
　　B. a smell of burning insulation　　D. all of the above

_____ **9.** One preventive maintenance action taken was to operate the overload trip mechanism every ___ months to check operation.

_____ **10.** ___ maintenance technician(s) was/were involved in the troubleshooting and repair of this problem.
　　A. One　　　　　　　　　　C. Four
　　B. Two　　　　　　　　　　D. none of the above

Troubleshooting Report

Maintenance Technician Identification Number: <u>6905, 3708</u>

Department: <u>Product line #6</u>

Equipment Identification Number: <u>Conveyor #34 drive motor - 163094</u>

Problem: <u>Conveyor not operating.</u>

Symptoms: <u>Loud snap and grinding heard. Smell of burning insulation. Conveyor stopped suddenly.</u>

Cause(s): <u>Chain broke and wrapped around drive sprocket while one end of the chain caught on the conveyor frame. The motor could not rotate and overheated because the overloads did not open. The overload trip mechanism was not functioning due to mechanical damage.</u>

Repair Procedures: <u>Replaced chain, motor, overloads, and magnetic motor starter.</u>

Preventive Maintenance Action: <u>Operate overload trip mechanism every six months to check operation. Chain should be inspected more frequently. Do not splice in new chain with old chain. Old and new chain was found on the broken chain.</u>

Troubleshooting Process

_____ **1.** Step 1　　**A.** Document

_____ **2.** Step 2　　**B.** Investigate

_____ **3.** Step 3　　**C.** Remedy

_____ **4.** Step 4　　**D.** Isolate

Electrical System Troubleshooting

_____ **1.** The DMM at A reads ___ V.

_____ **2.** The DMM at B reads ___ V.

_____ **3.** The DMM at C reads ___ V.

_____ **4.** The DMM at D reads ___ V.

_____ **5.** The DMM at E reads ___ V.

_____ **6.** The DMM at F reads ___ V.

_____ **7.** The DMM at G reads ___ V.

_____ **8.** The DMM at H reads ___ V.

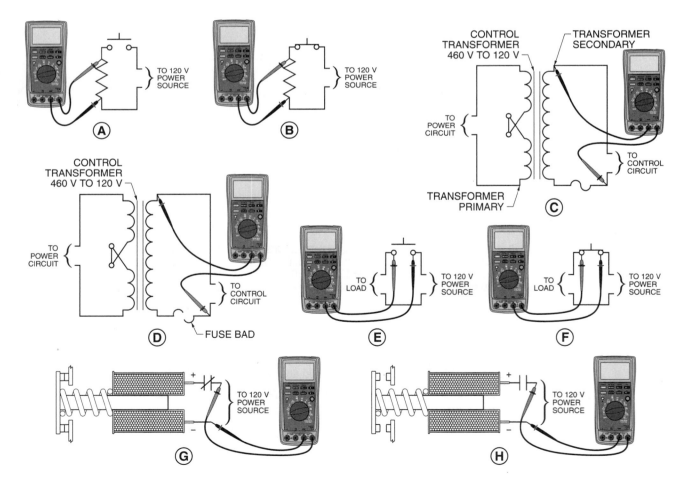

Name _____   **Date** _____

Activity 11-1. Garage Door Opener

A garage door opener found in a commercial application includes a motor to raise and lower the door, a control cabinet, and two limit switches.

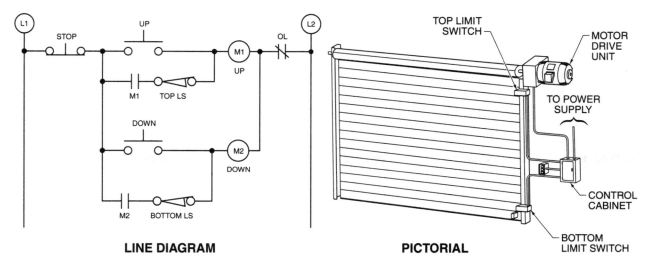

LINE DIAGRAM   **PICTORIAL**

1. If the top limit switch was out of alignment and would not open, what might happen to the motor when the door reached the top of its travel?

2. What mechanical problem could cause the garage door to stop halfway up?

3. How would the electrical circuit work if the bottom limit switch was misaligned and stayed open all the time?

4. Would it be possible to overload the motor if the bottom limit switch was misaligned and stayed closed all the time?

5. What type of mechanical damage to the stop button contacts could prevent the circuit from operating?

6. What electrical problem could result in the motor if the chain drive connecting the motor and garage door was misaligned?

Activity 11-2. Motor Control Circuit

A motor control circuit that controls three motors from a single start-stop pushbutton station is not operating correctly.

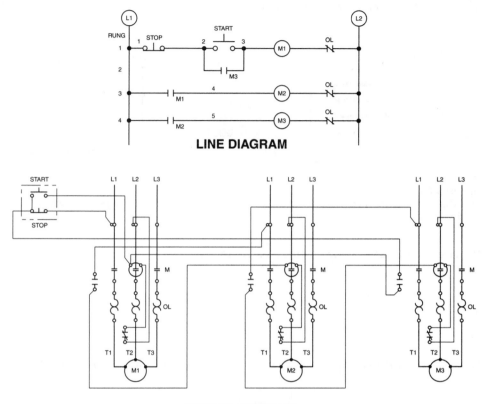

LINE DIAGRAM

WIRING DIAGRAM

1. List four possible causes for M2 not energizing.

2. How might a loose connection be located?

3. If M2 coil was open and would not energize, would M2 contacts on rung 4 close?

4. What is the likely problem if the fuse blows every time M2 is energized?

Activity 11-3. Heating Element Control

An electrical heating element is used to heat air in a HVAC system. A fan directs cool air through the duct and over the heating element, heating the air. An overheat temperature sensor near the element opens a normally closed switch in the electrical circuit when the temperature around the element exceeds a safe operating level.

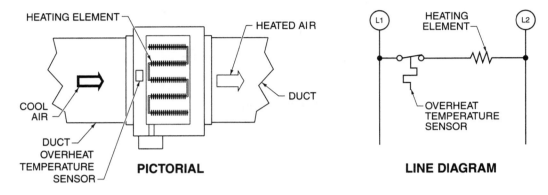

PICTORIAL   **LINE DIAGRAM**

1. What might cause the area around the heating element to overheat?

2. If the fan was working properly, what problem could cause a severe reduction in airflow?

3. What resistance reading would indicate that the heating element was bad?

4. If the heating element was open, what would the voltage reading across the heating element be if the overheat temperature sensor was also open?

5. If the heating element overheated and burned open, what additional device must have failed?

6. What preventive maintenance do electric heating elements require?

7. What are the primary safety concerns when working on this type of heating element?

8. If the voltage at the heating element was 0 V, would the fan in the air handler still be operating?

A separate HVAC system uses a set of three heating elements to heat air to a zone.

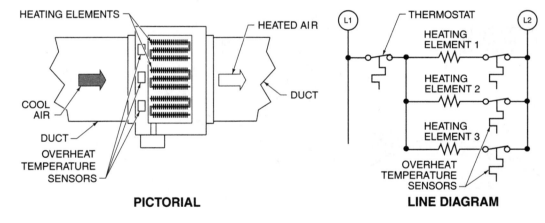

PICTORIAL   **LINE DIAGRAM**

9. If heating element 2 was open, would this affect the operation of the elements 1 and 3?

Activity 11-4. Paint Can Filling Operation

Three colors and a base are mixed to create paint of a specified color. Empty cans are spaced to arrive at the rotating can filler at a specific interval. A photoelectric sensor detects the shiny surface of the can liner and opens a gate in the filling machine for the can to enter. The can is filled as it moves through the filler and leaves on the outfeed conveyor. Another sensor detects the filled can and sends a signal for a lid to be placed on the can, which is then sealed by the can sealer.

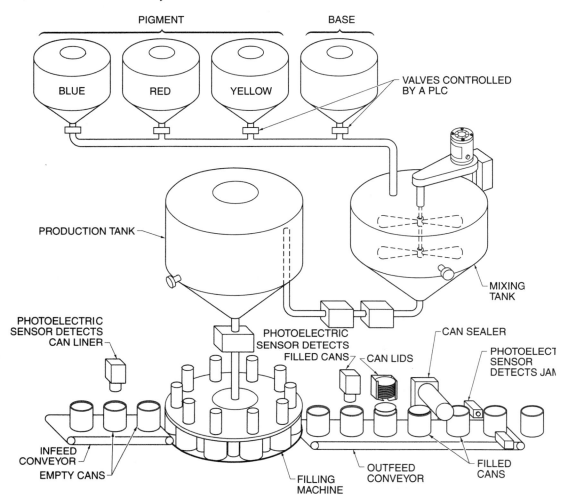

1. What preventive maintenance does the photoelectric sensor require?

2. What mechanical problem might cause the can lids to not be correctly placed on the cans?

3. What adjustment should be made if the can lids are not sealing tightly on the can?

4. What might cause the cans to leave the filling machine empty?

5. What might happen to the cans if a gate to enter the filling machine did not open?

6. List the systems that make up this process and the general maintenance inspections for each system.

Activity 11-5. PLC Inputs and Outputs

An input device is activated, sending a signal to the input module of a PLC and illuminating the corresponding input light. The central processing unit makes a decision based on the input signal. If the decision is to energize a load, then the central processing unit sends a signal to the out put module. An output light illuminates and the signal continues to the load, which energizes.

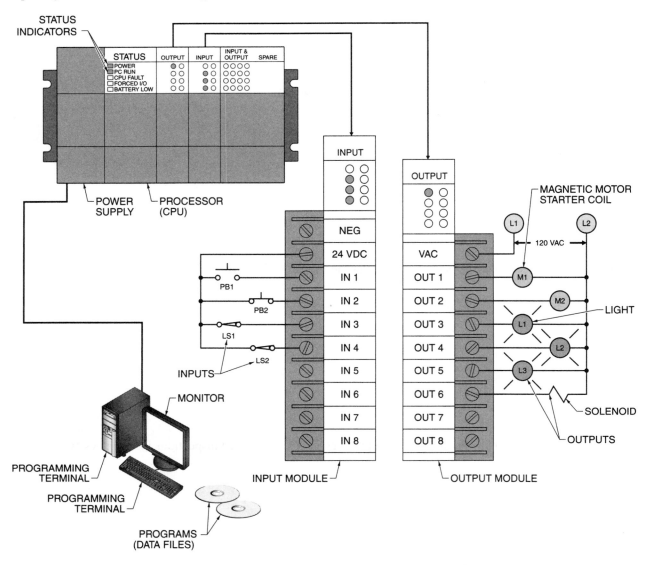

1. What might be the problem if PB1 is pressed but Input 1 does not light?

2. What might be the problem if Input 1 stays lit when PB1 is released?

3. What might be the problem if PB1 is pressed and Input 1 lights but Output 1 does not light as expected?

4. What might be the problem if PB1 is pressed and Output 6 lights but the solenoid does not energize?

5. What can be done if the program for the PLC is unintentionally altered and operating erratically?

6. If a load works when it is forced through the PLC program, but does not work when the inputs are operated, what is one likely cause of the problem?

Activity 11-6. Refrigeration Problems

The evaporator fan of a refrigeration unit is not operating.

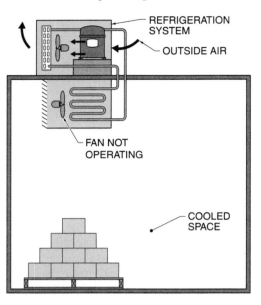

1. Would the pressure on the high-pressure side be higher or lower than normal?

2. Would the pressure on the low-pressure side be higher or lower than normal?

3. Would the superheat be higher or lower than normal?

4. Would the subcooling be higher or lower than normal?

5. What would happen to the temperature in the cooled space?

6. Would it be necessary to first attach a manifold gauge to determine the cause of the problem?

7. How might the compressor be damaged by this situation?

8. Could the evaporator ice up in this situation?

The condenser coils of a refrigeration unit are clogged with dirt.

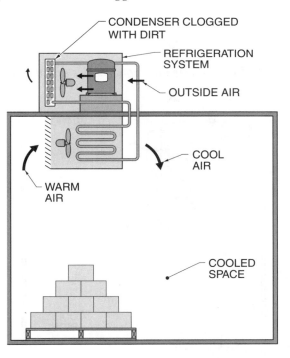

9. Would the pressure on the high-pressure side be higher or lower than normal?

10. Would the pressure on the low-pressure side be higher or lower than normal?

11. Would the superheat be higher or lower than normal?

12. Would the subcooling be higher or lower than normal?

13. What would happen to the temperature in the cooled space?

14. Would it be necessary to first attach a manifold gauge to determine the cause of the problem?

15. How might the compressor be damaged by this situation?

A refrigerant leak is suspected in the lines between the compressor and the condenser of a refrigeration unit.

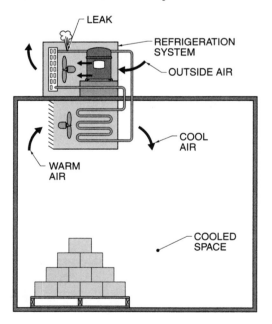

16. Would the pressure on the high-pressure side be higher or lower than normal?

17. Would the pressure on the low-pressure side be higher or lower than normal?

18. Would the superheat be higher or lower than normal?

19. Would the subcooling be higher or lower than normal?

20. What would happen to the temperature in the cooled space?

21. Would it be necessary to attach a manifold gauge to determine the cause of the problem?

22. How might the compressor be damaged by this situation?

23. How would the location of the leak be found?

24. If the leak repair required opening the system, what general procedures would be followed?

25. If the system contained R-22, what additional concern would affect the decision to repair or replace this system?

Activity 11-7. HVAC Troubleshooting

An office worker complains to the maintenance technician that the office space is too hot.

INVESTIGATE
Observed symptoms:
Outdoor temperature: 98°F
Relative humidity: 80%
Airflow to office: 220 CFM
Office temperature: 78°F
Cooling setpoint: 73°F

ISOLATE
Most likely causes of comfort problem:
- HVAC system cannot maintain the temperature because it is extremely hot outside with high relative humidity
- Poor airflow
- Radiant heat from windows or hot wall

1. What steps should be taken to solve this problem?

The system is working within specifications, but it is running most of the time. It is simply too hot outside for the system to maintain the setpoint temperature.

2. What should be done next?

REMEDY
Discuss remedies to this problem with the instructor, fellow students, or fellow workers.

DOCUMENTATION
3. What documentation might need to be filled out?

4. Why is clear, complete documentation important in this situation?

Activity 11-8. Coal Grinder

A grinder pulverizes coal for a large boiler. The coal is ground into a fine powder which is then blown into the boiler furnace where it is burned. A chain drive connects the conveyor motor to the conveyor pulley. The grinder motor is a three-phase, large-horsepower motor.

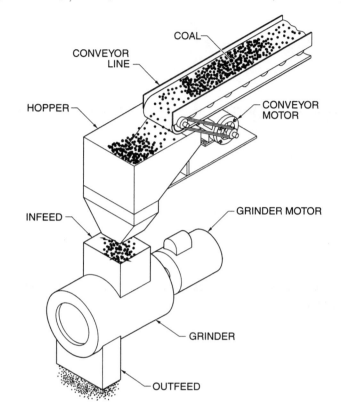

1. What is the most likely cause of conveyor chains wearing out quickly?

2. How could maintenance activities be adjusted for the chain and sprockets?

3. What monitoring equipment might be installed to protect the grinder motor?

4. What predictive maintenance activity would be appropriate for the grinder motor?

5. In addition to hard hats, safety glasses, and gloves, what additional piece of safety equipment might be required when working near the grinder?

6. What electrical problem might happen if two large motors like the grinder motor and conveyor motor were started at the same time?

Activity 11-9. Stopped Conveyor

A conveyor moving cases of motor oil to a loading area stops suddenly. It does not restart when the start pushbutton is pressed. There were no unusual sounds or other symptoms when the motor stopped.

INVESTIGATE
Observed symptoms:
Conveyor heavily loaded. No burning smell. No obvious mechanical damage.

ISOLATE
Most likely causes:
• Overload – mechanical or electrical
• Open in control circuit
• Burnt-out motor

Action/Results
• Tested overloads
Overloads were tripped. Reset overloads. Restarted conveyor and watched operation.

1. What is the likely cause of the overloads tripping?

2. Since the overloads were tripped, are the other possible causes worth pursuing?

3. What electrical measurement would determine if the motor was being overloaded?

4. What temporary solution could prevent the problem from reccurring?

5. If a larger horsepower motor was available and could be installed quickly, what factors should be considered when deciding whether to install it?

6. Why should the size of the overloads not be increased to allow the motor to run while overloaded?

7. What other sources of overload might there be in the conveyor?

8. What problems with the motor could be contributing to this overloading?

REMEDY
Discuss remedies to this problem with the instructor, fellow students, or fellow workers.

DOCUMENTATION

9. What documentation might need to be filled out?

Activity 11-10. Hydraulic Power Circuit

A hydraulic power circuit uses two directional control valves, each actuated by solenoids controlled by a PLC. One valve controls a hydraulic cylinder and the other controls a rotary actuator.

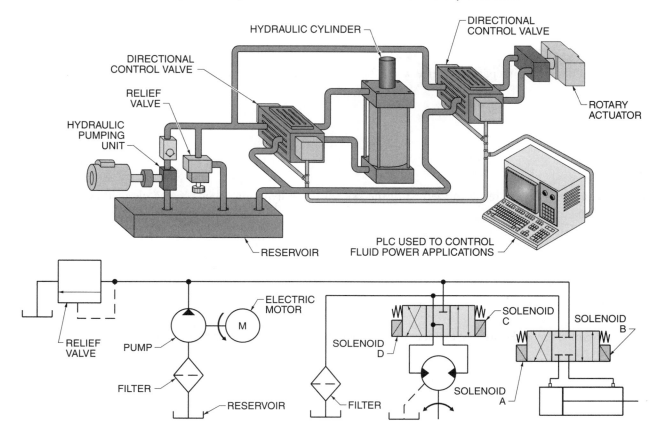

1. If solenoid A overheated and failed, which hydraulic device would be affected?

2. What would happen to system operation if the relief valve setting was too low?

3. What mechanical problem could prevent the cylinder from extending?

4. If power was lost to the PLC, would the hydraulic system continue to operate?

5. What predictive maintenance practice would be useful in maintaining the quality of the hydraulic oil?

6. What problems could result in the rest of the system if the hydraulic filter became clogged and the oil was bypassing the filter?

7. What problem could cause the cylinder to not stay in position when its directional control valve is in the neutral position?

8. How could the PLC be used to help troubleshoot the system?

9. What would happen to oil flow if the pump seals and valves were becoming worn?

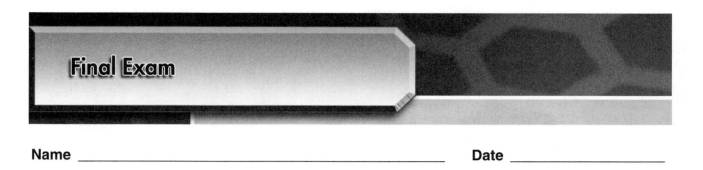

Final Exam

Name _____ **Date** _____

Industrial Maintenance

_____ **1.** An energy ___ is a comprehensive review of a facility's energy use and a report on ways to reduce the energy use through changes to buildings, equipment, and procedures.

_____ **2.** The NEC® is updated every ___ years.

_____ **3.** ___ is the United States representative to the ISO.

_____ **4.** Fuel, ___, oxygen, and a sustaining reaction are required to start and sustain a fire.

T   F   **5.** A regulation is an accepted reference or practice.

_____ **6.** ___ is the capacity to do work.

_____ **7.** ___ is force per unit area.

_____ **8.** ___ is the rate of doing work or using energy.

_____ **9.** A(n) ___ is the quantity of heat required to raise the temperature of 1 lb of water 1°F.

_____ **10.** ___ is the movement of an object by a force to a specific distance.

_____ **11.** Horsepower is a unit of power equal to ___.
    A. 746 W   C. 550 ft-lb/s
    B. 33,000 ft-lb/min   D. all of the above

_____ **12.** A(n) ___ is a substance that tends to flow or conform to the outline of its container.

_____ **13.** ___ is the measurement of the intensity of heat.

_____ **14.** ___ is the loss or removal of oxygen from a material.

_____ **15.** A(n) ___ is a subatomic particle that has a positive electrical charge of one unit.
    A. proton   C. electron
    B. neutron   D. all of the above

_____ **16.** ___ current is current that reverses its direction of flow at regular intervals.

_____ **17.** Current is measured in ___.
    A. volts   C. ohms
    B. amperes   D. none of the above

_____ **18.** ___ is the amount of electrical pressure in a circuit.

T   F   **19.** The larger the AWG number, the larger the diameter of the wire.

_____ **20.** Contacts fail when they ___.
    A. do not close   C. offer resistance to current flow
    B. do not open   D. all of the above

_____ **21.** A(n) ___ is a material that has little resistance and permits electrons to move through it easily.

_____ **22.** A(n) ___ is the smallest building block of matter that cannot be divided into a smaller unit without changing its basic character.

_____ **23.** ___ is the relationship between voltage, current, and resistance in a circuit.

T F **24.** All DC voltage sources have a positive and negative terminal.

_____ **25.** A(n) ___ drawing is a drawing that shows the length, height, and depth of an object in one view.

T F **26.** The fundamental line frequency in the U.S. is 60 Hz.

_____ **27.** A voltage surge is a ___ increase above the normal rated line voltage.
   A. 0%   C. 10%+
   B. 5%–10%   D. none of the above

_____ **28.** A ___ is a device that produces electricity when two different metals that are joined together are heated.
   A. thermistor   C. triac
   B. transducer   D. thermocouple

_____ **29.** A(n) ___ is a closed metal container (vessel) in which water is heated to produce steam or heated water.

_____ **30.** A low-pressure boiler is a boiler that has an MAWP of up to ___ psi.
   A. 15   C. 45
   B. 30   D. 60

_____ **31.** A boiler horsepower is the power available from the evaporation of ___ lb of water per hour at a feedwater temperature of ___°F.
   A. 1; 72   C. 100; 212
   B. 34.5; 100   D. none of the above

_____ **32.** A(n) ___ valve is a valve that allows flow in only one direction.

_____ **33.** A low water condition occurs when the water in a boiler is below the ___ as indicated by the gauge glass.

_____ **34.** Steam is produced as water is heated to ___°F and the water boils and turns from a liquid state to a gaseous state.

_____ **35.** ___ of a boiler is the recommended maximum pressure at which a boiler can safely be operated.

_____ **36.** The resistance of a 12 V circuit pulling 4 A is ___ Ω.

_____ **37.** A 120 V, 40 W load draws ___ A of current.
   A. 0.33   C. 160
   B. 3   D. 4800

_____ **38.** Change of ___ is the process that occurs when enough heat is added to or removed from a substance to change it from one physical state to another.

T F **39.** Heat flows only from a warmer temperature to a cooler temperature.

T F **40.** Charging is adding refrigerant to a system.

T F **41.** Substances exist in either a solid, liquid, or gaseous state.

_____ **42.** ___ is heat transfer that occurs when heat is passed from molecule to molecule through a material.

_____ **43.** ___ humidity is the amount of moisture in the air compared to the amount of moisture the air would hold if it were saturated.

T F **44.** The amount of moisture the air can carry depends on the air temperature.

T F **45.** Adding heat increases the energy content of a substance.

T F   **46.** Liquids cannot be compressed.

_____ **47.** Fan ___ is the volume of air a fan can move in a given period of time.

T F   **48.** The "too hot/cold" call is the most common HVAC system complaint encountered.

T F   **49.** Most HVAC systems are open-loop control systems.

T F   **50.** The efficiency of a filter is rated by the size of particles it can trap.

_____ **51.** ___ is the combination of metal and oxygen into metal oxides.

T F   **52.** Any two gears that mesh rotate in opposite directions.

_____ **53.** ___ is the measure of the resistance of a fluid's molecules to move past each other.

T F   **54.** An axial load is a load applied perpendicular to the rotating shaft.

T F   **55.** Safety is the most important concern when performing maintenance and troubleshooting work.

T F   **56.** If area is constant, force increases as pressure increases.

T F   **57.** If pressure is constant, force increases as area increases.

_____ **58.** ___ is an inward bursting.

_____ **59.** ___ is the three-dimensional size of an object.

T F   **60.** The warmer the air drawn into a compressor, the more efficiently the compressor operates.

_____ **61.** ___ is anything that changes or tends to change the state of rest or motion of a body.

_____ **62.** ___ energy is stored energy a body has due to its position, chemical state, or condition.

T F   **63.** A heat pump can switch between heating and cooling modes.

T F   **64.** Pneumatic systems usually operate at lower pressures than hydraulic systems.

_____ **65.** The severity of electrical shock is increased with less ___.

_____ **66.** Air normally contains ___% oxygen.

_____ **67.** ___ energy is energy of motion.

_____ **68.** ___ expansion is the change in volume of a material in relation to temperature.

T F   **69.** An analog multimeter indicates readings as digital values.

T F   **70.** DC voltage flows in one direction only.

_____ **71.** A ___ is a piece of equipment in which a large block of power is delivered and broken down into smaller units for distribution throughout a building.
     A. disconnect   C. lighting panel
     B. switchboard   D. none of the above

_____ **72.** A(n) ___ is an electronic component that allows current to pass in only one direction.

_____ **73.** A(n) ___ is a heat exchanger through which heat is transferred to the low-pressure refrigerant liquid.
     A. compressor   C. evaporator
     B. condenser   D. none of the above

_____ **74.** ___ force is the outward force produced by a rotating object.

Codes and Standards

_____ **1.** Publishes the National Electrical Code®.

_____ **2.** Acts as national coordinator and clearinghouse for consensus standards.

_____ **3.** Assists with information and standards concerning proper selection, ratings, construction, testing, and performance of electrical equipment.

_____ **4.** Acts in conjunction with OSHA to develop recommended exposure limits for hazardous substances or conditions located in the workplace.

_____ **5.** Tests equipment and products to verify conformance to national standards.

_____ **6.** Tests equipment and products to verify conformance to Canadian national standards.

_____ **7.** Requires employers to provide a safe working environment.

CSA	**UL**	**NFPA**	**NIOSH**	**NEMA**	**ANSI**	**OSHA**
Ⓐ	Ⓑ	Ⓒ	Ⓓ	Ⓔ	Ⓕ	Ⓖ

pH Scale

_____ **1.** Acidic

_____ **2.** Alkaline

_____ **3.** Neutral

_____ **4.** pH commonly required for boiler water

Lever Classes

_____ **1.** First class

_____ **2.** Second class

_____ **3.** Third class

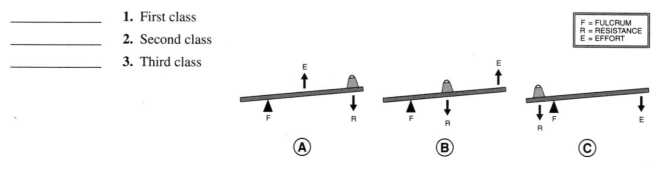

Temperature Conversion

_____ **1.** The temperature at A is equivalent to ___°C.

_____ **2.** The temperature at B is equivalent to ___°F.

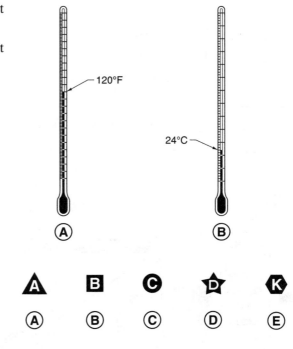

Fire Extinguisher Classes

_____ **1.** Ordinary combustibles

_____ **2.** Combustible metals

_____ **3.** Flammable liquids

_____ **4.** Electrical equipment

_____ **5.** Commerical oils

Stress

_____ **1.** Compression

_____ **2.** Bending

_____ **3.** Shear

_____ **4.** Tension

_____ **5.** Torsion

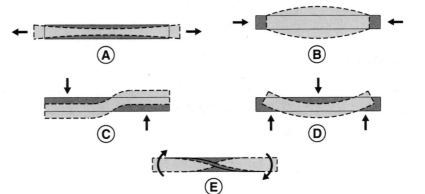

NFPA Hazard Signal System

_____ **1.** Fire hazard (red)

_____ **2.** Health hazard (blue)

_____ **3.** Specific hazard

_____ **4.** Reactivity (yellow)

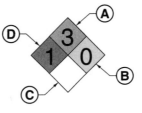

Mechanical Compression Refrigeration System

_____ **1.** Evaporator

_____ **2.** Compressor

_____ **3.** Condenser

_____ **4.** Cold air to cooled space

_____ **5.** Hot air

_____ **6.** Warm air from cooled space

_____ **7.** Warm outside air

_____ **8.** Vaporizing refrigerant

_____ **9.** Condensing refrigerant

_____ **10.** Liquid refrigerant

_____ **11.** Refrigerant vapor

_____ **12.** Filter-dryer

_____ **13.** Sight glass

_____ **14.** Metering device

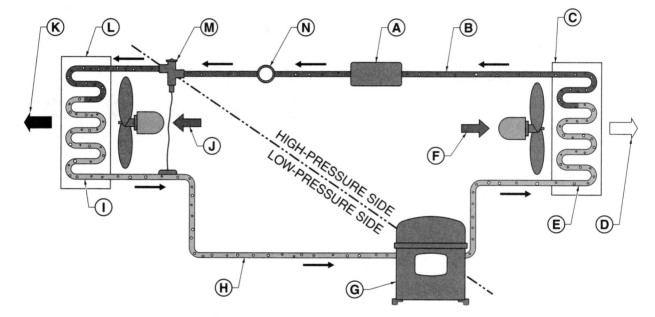

Ohm's Law

_____ **1.** The current at A is ___ A.

_____ **2.** The current at B is ___ A.

_____ **3.** The voltage at C is ___ V.

_____ **4.** The voltage at D is ___ V.

_____ **5.** The resistance at E is ___ Ω.

_____ **6.** The resistance at F is ___ Ω.

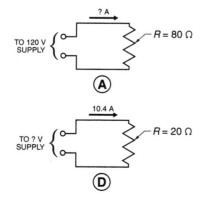

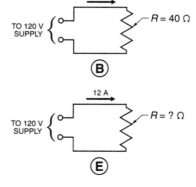

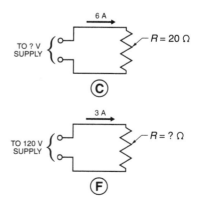

Appendix

Many maintenance and troubleshooting skills are learned on-the-job. Once fundamental skills are learned in the classroom, they are reinforced by applying them in the workplace. Learning is improved by working thoughtfully and by thinking about the work after it is completed.

The following forms include questions that address actual maintenance situations. The questions help the student carefully consider the planning, methods, and results of various maintenance tasks.

Preventive Maintenance Task Worksheet _____ 230
Work Order Checklist _____ 231
Work Order Plan and Results Comparison _____ 232
Work Order Debriefing _____ 233

Preventive Maintenance Task Worksheet

Technician: _____   Work Order Number: _____

What is the purpose of this piece of equipment?

What is the function of this piece of equipment in the larger system?

What is the purpose of the larger system?

How does this piece of equipment operate?

Why is this maintenance being performed? What problems will it prevent?

What else could go wrong with the piece of equipment? List two problems and their symptoms.

How could each problem be solved? How could each problem be prevented?

Work Order Checklist

Technician: _____ Work Order Number: _____

Actions	Comments	Date/Time
Work site investigated and information gathered		
Describe the purpose of the work		
Technical information or specifications located		
Planning worksheets completed		
Safety issues addressed		
Tools selected		
Parts selected or ordered		
Work started		
Completion date/time		
Work completed		
Work inspected		
Follow-up required		
Work order documented		

Comments:

Work Order Plan and Results Comparison

Technician: _____   Work Order Number: _____

Plan	**Results**
Step-by-step plan for completing work order.	What were the actual steps required?
Tools required.	What tools were used?
Safety plan.	What safety problems were encountered?
Parts required or ordered.	What parts were used?

Comments:

Work Order Debriefing

Technician: _____ Work Order Number: _____

What was learned from doing this work?

What skills were used?

What skills need to improve to complete similar work more efficiently?

What should be done differently for similar work in the future?

What should be done the same for similar work in the future?

How could the problem that caused this work order be prevented?